Formal Theories of Mass Behavior

Formal

Theories of

MASS

BEHAVIOR

William N.

McPhee

The Free Press of Glencoe

Collier-Macmillan Ltd., London

For information, address:
THE FREE PRESS OF GLENCOE
  A Division of The Macmillan Company,
  The Crowell-Collier Publishing Company
  60 Fifth Avenue, New York 11

TYPOGRAPHY BY MINA BAYLIS

Library of Congress Catalog Card Number: 62–15345

Collier-Macmillan Canada Limited, Galt, Ontario

To Minnow

Acknowledgments

Thanks are due first to those who subsidized this work with their vacations and weekends: Wendy, Jock, Sarah, and their mother and father in the dedication. Edmund deS. Brunner, Charles Glock, David Sills, and Clara Shapiro—in behalf of the Bureau of Applied Social Research—did not just preach theory but backed it here tangibly. Bernard Berelson placed crucial bets on this work earlier and then collected them himself by helping get out this and another 1962 report, with William Glaser.

If this book is in any tradition, it is embodied by Robert Lazarsfeld, a contrary ten-year-old. He has decided that in his time in sociology, the exciting uses of method will be in theory and, vice versa, the dramatic changes in theory will be in method. Yet his and mine is a strange "revolution"; the local government keeps sending us supplies. I have not asked Paul Lazarsfeld and Robert Merton to pretend even to the responsibility, however, of superficial reading of these examples completed when my absence prevented serious discussion.

James S. Coleman has been another corrupt influence, along with Lee M. Wiggins, whom I do not know whether to credit or exonerate. Currently, Jack Ferguson, Robert B. Smith, and Harry Milholland deserve credit far beyond coauthored papers in this program. Myra Gordon ran the current project for us. Production at The Free Press was by Katherine Purcell, charts by Lorraine Blake. Chapter 4 is by courtesy of *The Public Opinion Quarterly*.

I save as last the crucial credits: to the former Behavioral Sciences Division of the Ford Foundation and now to the Social

Science Division of the National Science Foundation—as well as to their support of the Center for Advanced Study in the Behavioral Sciences, where this book was completed—for their backing of intangibles other than data collection. The latter is essential, but as the data now pile up, "parsimony" is proving expensive too.

Contents

Formal Theories of Mass Behavior

Introduction

This book is written for nonmathematical audiences. If social scientists and research practitioners with humanistic backgrounds could not enjoy it, I would be talking to myself. Not just read but enjoy it; there is fun in this book, but it is in the substance, not the formalities.

Indeed, mathematics would never be discussed in this style. The book is full of stories—redundant interpretation, concrete examples, and digressions to apply each theory to live data. And especially it is full of pictures—diagrams, flow charts, and illustrative tabulations. I am not talking down to anyone; social scientists know the subtleties in their own business. I am simply making sure the formal language is translated into substantive language.

The book is not didactic, however. If it is to be taken seriously as social theory—within its assigned limits to specific problems that I know well enough to say such definite things about—then I have to go to work on these problems and cannot keep stopping to give instruction on something else that I am not qualified to teach even to freshmen. Therefore, the reader who has trouble with mathematics, as we all do, has to follow sensible rules for reading, yes, reading, the substance of the book:

1. Do *not* skip lightly over—rather stop and study for easy going later—the notation and model in the first part of each paper. These are the concepts and relationships of the theory, of course, without which one is as lost in the sequel as he would be in Talcott Parsons.

2. *Do* skip all the remaining formulas that are not self-evident in a moment or two, as most are. The others have the same status as technical tables in research and extended citations in scholarship: not something to feel "lost" about if one can't follow them on first reading. If they have any import I can see, it is discussed in the text.

There is a straw man in this "reading," however, and let us knock it down now. The technical reviewer will run into some awfully strong verbal interpretations; but, since the last thing I find social scientists lack is the quarrelsome instinct, it is not surprising that in trial readings—and the same has been true of professors of English, psychiatrists, and television executives—the first thing they do is come back and bite the interpretation that led them into the formal argument in the first place. That is all it is here for.

So much for reading the book: anyone can. The primary audience the text is written for—because the research fraternity will not need urging to see applications—is the theorist and teacher of social science as theory. Someone has traced back two centuries of preaching for mathematical theory in social affairs, but outside of economics and now some portions of psychology, it has been futile preaching. I want to devote this Introduction to showing how fundamentally that situation has changed because of sudden technological luck, which gives a completely different picture of the uses of formal reasoning in social theory. These new prospects are discussed under three headings:

1. Some "New Games"
2. The Modular Approach
3. Standard Processes

Then the book itself will be devoted to concrete examples.

SOME "NEW GAMES"

By "new games" I mean partly the literal sense—that some strange pursuits we have never seen before are now going on—but mostly I intend a figurative meaning taken from sports:

a previously hopeless situation suddenly becomes, because of some unforeseen break, one in which we start all over again with completely new prospects (and in this case, new rules as to who can play the game). These unforeseen developments are discussed below in three areas: (1) social theory, (2) social research, and (3) mathematical social science.

Verbal Theory and Deductive Power

Social theorists have assumed that anything called a "computer" must have its application in research statistics. Actually, it is a dichotomous logic machine. The misnomer, "computer," was given only to the first triumph: one could get it to add! Because it is a logic machine, however, two things have since been replaced: the old desk calculators *and* the clerks who did all of the qualitative things. Replacing the latter makes for the new game in social theory.

Suppose that, instead of asking the new "desk calculators" to explore the numerical consequences of a mathematical model too complex to solve, we ask the equivalent of a few thousand of the new "clerks," working over a generation, to be symbols and structures and people acting out the consequences of a qualitative theory too complex even to think about. Neither the machine *nor* a philosopher of science could tell the difference.

There are difficulties in both, but they are common to both. The problem I consider central is what the examples in this book are about, but this is going to be a long haul. The problem the social science reader considers the *sine qua non*, however, is already solved. It is, how can social theory that speaks English instruct those "clerks" who listen only to logic?

A computer "language" is a program to translate from prearranged symbols convenient for the user into whatever logical nonsense—no matter *how* complicated—is necessary to carry out the process. The first-generation languages have already translated alphabetic symbols. One of the second-generation language, Newell, Shaw, and Simon's "Information Processing Language"

(IPL), did an absolutely remarkable job on taking the otherwise prohibitive work out of nonnumerical, "qualitative" programing.[1]* It is becoming standard in psychological work, but for mechanical reasons in large-scale problems, "social" social scientists are urged to look into a third generation of such languages, of which I choose the example of Markowitz's "Simscript," now in testing, as one that looks most promising for simulation of social processes at this writing.[2] It not only speaks (incorporates the gains of) the old languages under the surface, but *on* the surface it makes explicit where they were headed: it speaks English!

For instance, 150 carefully thought-out English sentences, stating the processes of a model, were recently compiled (translated) into 8,000 logical operations necessary to carry them out. And when set in motion, typically 100 million logical events or perhaps one million meaningful interactions would intervene between the 150 simple process descriptions and their consequences of interest. One thing, therefore, is certainly new. We have always had a geometry corresponding to spatial reasoning, an algebra corresponding to numerical reasoning, and a calculus corresponding to motion reasoning, but we have apparently had no deductive machinery ever corresponding to verbal reasoning. Many would say there still is none, but I agree with those who say there has always been one, logic. What is new is the capacity to do *enough* logic to find out what 150 carefully chosen English sentences are implying!

Research and Aggregation

Let us turn now to a second old impasse that also merits a new look. Most of our modern social research is irretrievably *microscopic;* that is, it is only about individuals in the mass. And it is irretrievably *discrete*, persons sampled out of structures and facts taken out of the flow of processes. For all the complaint about it,

* Footnotes begin on page 24.

this is the level that is accessible to know definite things about. Yet because it is so observable, the research often seems "obvious." What we cannot grasp—our theory cannot cope with it either, since its tests end in arguments over statistical significance —is the aggregated dynamics of social significance.[3]

What the new logic machines are teaching us is no wonder! The simplest models *do* get into a million significant interactions in processing microscopic data from empirical studies to reach (simulate) significant macroscopic conclusions—or what would be "conclusions" if, at the moment, we were not also having trouble figuring them out in our own models! But that itself is a symptom of the enormous span it is, the "micro-macro" span as it occurs in sociology.

The trick that some of us have been trying, in this impasse, has not "solved" the problem of spanning the micro-macro gap, but it is a way to do *research* on that problem. For instance, a model of voting is touched on in this book and described in detail elsewhere.[4] The voting processes in it, mentioned below, behave very differently, depending on properties of the individual going through them. That is, parameters unique to him make the process unique for him. Why not, then, let these parameters be specified by the properties of a *real* individual interviewed in a survey? Since a computer can handle thousands of such theoretical individuals simultaneously, each following processes specified by his parameters, then why not represent every individual in a community or state or national sample, so that the theoretical population "is" a real population? And then why not set the model in motion, in response to political appeals that themselves have an empirical basis (explained in Chapter 4 here)? In a word, why not explore the macroscopic implications of such real facts *dynamically?*

Logically, this proposal is no different from what is done with dynamic mathematical models, in this book, for example. On this enormous scale, however, which is like a whole population interacting, it is so realistic that one shivers. We have tried it only with a short-term version of the voting model, re-creating the few months of the 1956 campaign with a nationwide sample taken just before it and re-creating the month of the 1960 presidential primary campaign in Wisconsin with a statewide sample taken before it, as illustrated in Chapter 4 here. There is no reason, however, that one cannot go on and explore dynamic implications of contemporary data—what they indicate is possible, likely, and so on—all the way to 1984! It has precisely the 1984 air about it (although it is not that "good," thank God). In any event, there is no stopping a theory that starts with contemporary data from going on to 2084 and 2184, as Jack Ferguson plans to draw aggregate consequences from a model of social mobility that will be "raising the children of the children of the children" of the people that can be interviewed today.[5] This is certainly a new game, at the least.

Mathematics and Complexity

It is a form of dynamic aggregation, however, like a giant integral calculus. Nothing is more impossible to analyze verbally than dynamics.[6] Moreover, even when sophisticated numerical methods are applied, the above kind of work remains empirical-like in flavor.[7] Sooner or later, then, one is brought around to examining a third old impasse, that which surrounds mathematical social theory. Social scientists raise all the wrong issues about mathematical theory. For example, they think it means a commitment to positivistic "science" (not in this book!) or to "quantitative" theory (in this book, yes, counting, but only because of my particular interests in mass processes). Mathematical readers, however, know the Achilles' Heel that hurts: the restriction to simplicity.

A virtue is made of that necessity, simplicity, but this virtue can approach sterility in social applications, because of the uniquely *observable* nature of social affairs. Suppose something really is simple enough to be tractable. Then it tends to be "obvious" to those who have, indeed, lived it all their lives. Suppose, however, it is not simple, as, for example, international relations are not. Then the necessary oversimplification is intolerably "visible" in social affairs. For example, since students of international affairs know a hundred times more about international arms races than Lewis Richardson's model of that topic could cope with analytically,[8] his model was never taken seriously.

What is simple a lifetime participant in social affairs knows, and what he does not know is *not* simple. Therefore, why do I persist in the obvious or the oversimplified in this book? Let the reader ask himself under what conditions will he not only tolerate oversimplification but also *welcome* the analytical control it gives? It is when one intends to use these simple things in combinations to attack complex things.

And that is the new game that the logic machines make possible in applying mathematics to social theory. It is a new capacity to *combine* the elementary things one can best understand mathematically to attack the complex things he would like to understand socially.[9] For example, the model of so-called "voting" mentioned before was actually designed to study aggregate electoral dynamics, for example, self-equilibration capacities of electoral systems *as* systems; but let us neglect the social structures involving many voters, and the political strategies involving many stimuli, that the "system" problems require. They are unnecessary to make the point. Merely to get the *individual* voting done, it takes a combination of three processes in interaction over time. For example, the one not otherwise discussed in this book is a learning process that can be simplified into an analog of G. Polya's urn model of "after-effects."[10] The technical reader will recall from the many ramifications of Polya's process throughout serious texts like Feller's on probability that this is not trivial mathematically. Each of the other two processes in our voting model, taken *alone*, is also about the limit of tractability.

On the other hand, the social scientist will see in this book how necessary it is to have the combination of all three processes *interacting*—one is needed just to receive political stimuli, another just to learn from them psychologically, and another just to transmit what was learned as social heritage, or one process per discipline involved! This is the minimum complexity needed to reproduce the elementary facts of voting. Not rightly, just *at all*. The minimum is about three times the maximum that is tractable.

To be able to remove such restrictions on complexity—for practical if not for mathematical purposes—is certainly a new game in any event. It is not only that mathematical theory is now "complicatable" enough to reach social complexity, but some of us are also finding that, given realistic social complexity, we want it "uncomplicatable" back down again into simpler components that can be analyzed mathematically. If anybody has been oversimplifying, it has been both sides on this puzzle: it is not to do away with either, but how to have our complexity and analyze it too?

THE MODULAR APPROACH

The last question above has many other versions. How can one have complexity and yet simplify it too, so that complicated things can be *created* in reasonable time? How can one have complications and yet control them too, so that complex creations can be *trusted* in the same way one can know what he is doing with simple things? And especially, how can one have complexity and yet standardize it too, so that complicated things, which tend to be complicated uniquely, can nevertheless be *generalized?*

There is a well-known answer to such problems—problems of taming complexity. The record shows that every field suddenly confronted with new powers to do things vastly more complex than before had to learn the same lessons for itself. Three such lessons must be discussed: (1) upgrading conceptual equipment for power, (2) downgrading conceptual equipment for generality,

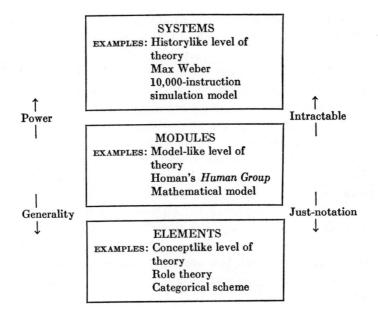

Figure 1

and (3) treating systems as "modular configurations." To see what these mean, it is first useful to consider Figure 1.

By a "system" I mean, to be concrete, a virtually self-sufficient factory, a complete 7090 computer installation all linked together, or the U.S. electoral system (completed by including all the officeholders). This level of big and therefore autonomous systems is the one with greatest *power*, that is, power to *do* extraordinary things. If we had theory adequate to model such a complete system, it would have so much deductive power we could get as lost in its implications as in history itself.

At the opposite end of the scale from power lies *generality*. At the bottom in Figure 1, I use the name "elements." An element in a factory is a bolt or wheel, in a 7090 computer a wire or transistor. These are wonderful ideas, but each is weak alone. It is no criticism, but praise of generality, to say that this is where most of our modern technical social theory lies. It is conceptualization, the individual units in which are conceptual elements like "role." Even Talcott Parsons' work is mostly at this level. His is not a theory of "a" system, not like Marx, for example. Parsons is ambitious in the opposite direction of generality.[11]

Unhappily, the price of generality is usually loss of power. A bolt or a transistor or a notational scheme in mathematics—or a concept like role—can be called a "powerful idea" in the sense of its generality, its wide usefulness; but strictly speaking, it can *do* little by itself. This limitation is especially true of deductive power. Definitions have almost none; one process little more. It is only by adding more assumptions that deductive power multiplies combinatorially; but then the cost of power is loss of generality. The struggle between the two is what the game of parsimony is all about, but this is *not* the game social scientists play, which is virtually to give up (deductive) power in favor of (empirical) generality.

Upgrading for Power

What the new possibilities make us appreciate, however, is that this can be generality *ad absurdum* for our purposes, that is, for attacking socially significant complexity. To see why, try to visualize what an incredible task it is to build a complete model of a social system that really *is* a system. For example, Hogatt and Balderston built a dynamic model of a market (consisting of producers, wholesalers, and retailers) all the way up from decision rules for the individuals involved and communications between them; but the several years' work in building it so exhausted them that, while the model works—remarkably on first try—at this writing no one has yet recovered the strength to analyze it.[12] At Columbia we have had less patience: we never quite finish, not through to a complete system. The model for analyzing electoral systems mentioned before is complete as a theory only through the voting in detail. The rest is only broadly provided for, and details must be supplied as input, *ad hoc*. A model of "mass culture systems" discussed below and represented here by a component, Chapter 3, is otherwise unfinished business.

What is the difficulty ? It is an old one in the history of dealing with complexity. To build up realistic social systems from conceptual equipment at the elementary level we now have is like having to build up the large factories of the nineteenth century all the way from bolts and wheels. Or it is like building up the first large computers all the way from wire and tubes. Or, as an intellectual task very close to ours, it is like building the first computer programs complicated enough to do anything unobvious—play chess, for example—all the way up to machine instruction by machine instruction, into thousands. All these things had to be done, but anyone who tries it, to create something vastly more complicated than before, quickly gets a jaundiced view of the old equipment.

It is too general. For that means: too *elementary*.

For example, the idea of a wheel is very "basic," it is true; but no one tries to build up factories from wheels and bolts any more. Instead, engineering had to *upgrade* standardization, from standard wheels and bolts to standard industrial machine tools like automatic lathes. The difference is that the latter *do* more per standard unit. As another example, a wire or tube or transistor is very "fundamental," but no one builds up computer installations out of them any more. Again, standardization has had to be upgraded—from standard tubes to standard memory banks. These are called "modules." As another example, 10,000-instruction computer programs are under complete intellectual control today, for they are not jerry-built out of individual instructions, but largely out of proven "sub-routines."[13] Again, it is standardization on units that *do* much more per unit.

And this is the important thing illustrated by the examples of this book. They show a comparable kind of "upgrading" of the power of conceptual tools, for purposes of coping with socially significant complexity. Upgrading is not meant in a value sense, but in a technical sense of power to do much more, go much farther, and say much more, *per unit* of conceptual equipment. Indeed, a valuable thing has to be sacrificed—generality—for what one learns is that "general" means "elementary" and "elementary" means "gets nowhere" in the face of truly complex problems.

An example of what upgrading the power of conceptual units means is, for instance, Chapter 5, "On the Logic of Addiction." This paper first presents a typology of six separate kinds of motive forces prominent in discussions of addictive-like "pursuits." This is a typical conceptual scheme. What Chapter 5 adds as the additional power, however, is to combine these motivational forces as parameters in the same model (as the "underlying" motivational forces in it). Then it takes a very long Chapter 5 merely to outline—by analysis of all the logical implications—the dozens and dozens of known things the theorist is saying when he says only *one* thing: that this kind of model is operative.

Mathematics, however, is *not* essential to it. Rather, what is required of the theory and theorist is a greater completeness of ideas within a conceptual unit, so that it is a little system itself. Chapter 2, "A Theory of Informal Social Influence," is entirely a qualitative idea. All it does is to *complete* Kurt Lewin's well-known qualitative idea, "social reality"; but when completed, it has surprisingly extended deductive ramifications—the reader will see, it does so many things—as *one* conceptual unit.

But isn't this just "a long way around" for sociologists and political scientists to discover what everyone else knows, the power of an explicit model? Yes, but what a difference "the long way around" makes in explaining its *use*. For example, of what use are the two little models above? Social influence is what half of social psychology is about. Addiction, as the other example, is a whole family of fields. Specialists in either topic would argue these models are too oversimplified to be of use to them. I disagree, and this book shows why. But I agree in the following sense. If I seem to be urging a mathematical model as the theory of its *own* subject matter, I am talking oversimplification where most people find it intolerable: in their own specialty.

But I have already mentioned the different use for the social-influence model. It is not only for its own interest. It is a subpart of a voting model that, in turn, is a subpart of larger systems put together for studying electoral dynamics. And the purpose of the addiction model of Chapter 5 is also to get at a larger problem. That can be called the "ecology of motivation." I intend, and hope others will, to study *communities* of interest in addictive-like pursuits—the symbiotic relations therein. This problem can be studied in large simulation models, with the ecology not the addiction as the subject matter, but *not* if each theorist has to spend several years just finding core processes, as I did in the voting case, merely to do the elementary work of getting individuals addicted to whatever pursuit one is interested in. That is not necessary now. The model in Chapter 5 is shown to be indefinitely adaptable for use in any such problem.

In this sense such models can be accepted as "standard (sub) units" for portraying details in larger problems of interest to a sociologist, without his taking any position on whether mathematical models as simple as these are serious theories of their *own* subject matter, that is, of its psychology. I think they are, but one thing I know: social theorists will never cope with significant complexity—if we ever finish the larger models necessary, most will be so jerry-built as to collapse into absurdities—unless we develop the building blocks for it at this intermediate level of *already* powerful conceptual units. What I mean by such units is what the examples of this book illustrate.

Downgrading for Generality

Now the question arises, what is the appropriate size or level of function one needs performed by a single conceptual unit? Or, if one wishes, what size should a "standard problem" in such work be? There are two compelling reasons dictating a certain limit on the complexity and therefore on the size of the standard problems.

One is a straight practical matter. For future reasons, one has to keep subunits simple enough ultimately to be tractable for mathematics and statistics. This was originally *not* cogent for me, rather the problems of generality below, but it turns out that a process that is elementary enough to be general is also simple enough to be tractable, at least in my own work. This is a happy finding. The next section suggests how a whole nexus of questions of "truth" and generalization depend on the ultimate tractability of subunits in the theory. For the moment, consider the other limit on the size of the subunits that are "standardizable."

As complicated things, big systems tend to get too *particular*. No two factories, for example, are alike. The same is tending to be true of the models of big social systems. Hogatt and Balderston's model was inspired by the West Coast lumber industry; the subunits of it would be what are general. And as for the so-called "voting" model, I doubt if as many as a dozen people in the country are interested in using the particular configurations one must build up, on a rather *ad hoc* basis, to study the problems of complete electoral systems that interest me.

About the most general we have yet been able to get at this social system level—and not lose the deductive power altogether in *just* generalities—is a model of "the mass culture system" that Professor Samuel Becker of the University of Iowa and I loosely specified and partly programed several years ago.[14] It is to be for studying problems common enough to the movies, popular music, television, and the like to treat together; but that is scarcely "general." Powerful social systems are complicated and therefore tend to be complicated uniquely.

But within a larger model one notices many things that are general. For example, consider a process used in the mass-culture system above for "exposing" consumers to information about the cultural alternatives available to them, to information on best sellers, for example. When taken *alone*, this is a widely useful process. Perhaps nothing is more general in mass social affairs than "haphazard exposure": to chance information, to contact with ethnic groups, to experiences, to ideas, and the like. Therefore, the exposure process is formalized as Part I of Chapter 3 here, called "Natural Exposure," as a basic unit that can be used elsewhere.

The point, then, is that considerations of generality force the level of conceptual standardization *down*, far below the maximum power that is otherwise possible with the new technology.

System as Modular Configuration

Yet who is to say what is "general"? The question of generality is always such a frustrating problem of persuasion in social theory. One keeps trying to persuade others to use his conceptualization, but they try to persuade him to use theirs. Since neither succeeds, we always border on Babel. A delight in the present work, then, is that there is no such persuasion problem.

It is so *difficult* to get a dynamic process that will work properly and that is tractable in ways discussed below that the borrowing from one another is automatic. For example, the "learning" process of the voting model, described earlier as a Polya process, has been used with adaptations suggested by Ithiel de S. Pool and James S. Coleman to model the development of "favorites" among television programs, as part of a larger model of attention to all mass media.[15] Similarly, the "social-influence" process above, a variant of Lewin's ideas, has been taken over from the voting model for use in another model of problems like college students' decisions, representing students' influence on one another.[16]

We will shortly see the compelling reasons that I have been borrowing too, but notice in the cases above that, for example, attention to the mass media has little to do with voting. So, one component borrowed from a voting model is now imbedded in an otherwise different configuration of very different processes in the media simulation. This imbedding of *standard* units, each of a self-contained nature, in an infinite variety of *particular* configurations, has an old name: the "modular approach" to complicated systems.

For instance, the attempt at mass production (a form of generalization) of big computers has had to be virtually abandoned. Each user's needs are different. Therefore, standardization has been forced to come "down" to a level of less powerful units—memory banks, printers, and the like. The essential idea is this: big systems are no longer treated as primary units but as *configurations* of (lesser) primary units.

This idea of big systems as *ad hoc*, whereas the primary units that are standardized are instead at a middle level, was hailed as "the solution" to mass production in the earlier part of this century—and indeed it was. It is merely so natural now that no one remembers the dawning of the idea. It was not just the realization that one did not need to build factories up all the way from wheels and bolts but *also* that one did not have to "standardize factories," as had seriously seemed to be the only alternative.[17] Similarly, the only alternative some of us saw to building huge simulation models up from elementary conceptual tools was, for a time, trying to "generalize" (standardize) a few such big systems. An interesting effort of that kind is Herbert A. Simon's "General Problem Solver."[18] When this can be done, we are indeed in luck, but the general solution in social affairs—where the number and heterogeneity and thus the particularity of significant systems is so great—will surely have to be the modular approach.

Namely, it is to treat the big models of socially significant systems as configurations of self-contained "little systems," representing the standard functions that are generalizable across the too-particular large systems. The big configurations will surely be the "spectaculars," the major prizes at stake in the use of the new technology, but it is not an either-or choice. If self-contained units in them can be identified that have real power that is nevertheless widely applicable in new configurations, then we can have our complexity and generalize it too.

STANDARD PROCESSES

It remains to get down to cases on what "standard" could mean in the case of modules of social theory. Let us discuss what I mean by standard in connection with generalizing the concrete examples of this book. They are first introduced under a main heading, (1) generalization of content. Then we will conclude with brief comments on unfinished business: (2) generalization of structure and (3) generalization of method.

Content Generalization

For reasons of personal interest and editorial motivation, I give every model in this book a very specific interpretation, but I have no confidence in the generalizability of such interpretations of social affairs. Wide application is impossible unless models are freed of their content. Instead, logical *structure* is what is general in them, as follows.

SURVIVAL AND DECAY. Chapter 1 illustrates specifically the survival of cultural creations such as operas or television programs, hence the title "Survival Theory in Culture." But the general situation is this: heterogeneous materials are continually being put into some device, for example, items of information into a brain. Then these continuously disappear or decay, but there are different probabilities or different rates of decay for different material. Thus, the final composition of what still survives at some equilibrium point—for example, what a brain typically remembers—is of very different composition from what has been put in. Chapter 1 gives a model for representing and analyzing such situations, that is, what the equilibrium composition consists of. This general sort of model would apply in dozens if not hundreds of social applications: to the survival of employees constantly being recruited into an organization, to the survival of marriages of heterogeneous original quality, or to the survival of youths through the eliminations of upward social mobility.

FILTERING. I use *filtering* to generalize the problem of Chapter 2, "A Theory of Informal Social Influence."[19] Earlier, this problem was called Kurt Lewin's social-reality idea; it is. Originally, however, I had in mind a "reconsideration" idea. Then the paper shows that the completed model ends up not too different from "reinforcement" ideas in behaviorism. What is the idea then? This illustrates a point discussed below: *interpretations* are highly variable, a virtual Babel in sociology, but freed of their content, how many are talking about really distinct logical ideas?

A filtering notion, in any event, applies wherever there is a prior mechanism that has a partly stochastic output, such as a son's impressions from time to time of what he favors on the political scene. It also requires some subsequent mechanism that uses (in this case cumulates) some of these stochastic outputs, such as the son's impressions that become ingredients out of which his political party loyalty is formed. Then the "filter" plays the role of *selecting* which outputs of the prior stochastic mechanism reach the subsequent using or cumulating mechanism, for example, as a father selects which of the randomlike political preferences of a son are encouraged. As another instance, critics filter the highly variable outputs of artists or writers, with respect to which of their creations are widely used and thus cumulate as the artist's reputation. As another example, an individual filters from the many random contacts he makes, the few that will cumulate as friendships.

EXPOSURE. Exposure to such random contacts, for instance, are the next problem, in Chapter 3, "Natural Exposure and the Theory of Popularity." As the generality of exposure has been discussed, a word should be said about Part II of the paper, on "popularity." This is not a dynamic process, but is an example of a standard *problem*. Any ranking of alternatives by popularity runs into a snarl of unhappy social implications as soon as we make the slightest logical inquiry into whether this is a "fair" or "proper" way to make a group decision. Black, Arrow, and others have analyzed such problems in politics and economics; but as both Chapter 3 and Chapter 1 illustrate, I recommend to the mathematically trained reader that it is no longer the problems of political and economic democracy, but of *cultural* democracy that are the logical nightmares of our century.

STIMULATION. Chapter 4, "A Campaign Simulator," is unhappily brief; but it is the crude beginning of what I consider the most valuable idea in the book. Indeed, we will see it is in good company.

Call it "stimulation theory." To explain it by contrast, call much of what underlies psychometrics "response theory." In the latter, the analyst is first given observed responses. By postulating a theory of how they originated, he solves his model for (estimates of) the underlying parameters. One dominant theme in such theories, coming down from Thurstone, is that there is not "a" response to a stimulus, but a *distribution* thereof, from which the observed responses are samplings. He called these "discriminal" distributions, from pyschophysics.[20] But in social affairs most modern writers would locate the variability—variable from one time to the next and from one person to the next —chiefly in differences of perceptual circumstances for each individual. So we call aggregates of this variability, *perceptual distributions*.

Now, what I mean by "stimulation theory" is the other side of the coin from the response theory of psychometrics. What the work reported in Chapter 4 stumbled onto—embarrassingly innocent of any thought of Thurstone—was the reverse idea of measuring the perceptual distributions as *observables* in advance of some event requiring responses to them. Then one can infer the probable responses by a theory of how people sample from these distributions of possible perceptions and respond to what they perceive (by standard scaling assumptions). This sounds innocent enough, but the interested reader is urged to see its development in subsequent work.[21] For it is on its way toward giving a formal meaning to an old and elusive idea, the "effect" of communications appeals.

AUTOMOTIVATION. Chapter 5, "The Logic of Addiction," concerns processes that depend heavily on their *own* recent level of activity. An example is the stock market. Another is conforming behavior with respect to some noxious duty. We slack off, but the slacking off itself finally requires activity to catch up. Falling in love is also "automotivated" activity: the more one sees the girl, the more he wants to see her. But with a change in parameters, this can be a model of "satiation," a classic automotivated phenomenon where activity generates its own cessation.

Thus, interpretations are as infinitely varied as social affairs themselves. But if we cumulate work around the logical structure of situations, rather than their interpretative content, isn't the former structure also capable of infinite permutation? In principle, yes. In practice, it is not working out that way. I have just mentioned about how a "new" idea about communications effects boils down to Thurstone's ideas of the 1930's. In the voting model, a "new" learning process turned out to be Polya's model of after-effects.

A well-known recent case was that of Estes' elaborately motivated learning theory. It was discovered to reduce, algebraically, to the same thing as the behavioristic model formulated independently by Bush and Mosteller. And if the reader will take a look in the Technical Note of Chapter 5, where I discovered it myself, he will see what my elaborate motivations of an "addiction" model can be reduced to algebraically. Except for one term, which the learning models should probably have also, it comes out like an Estes-Bush-Mosteller model! Since I refuse to believe that learning is addiction, or all addiction is learning, it is for good reason I call these models by a term as general as "automotivated" processes.

To sum up, I agree it is absolutely hopeless to speak of standardization or generalization of the *interpretation* of social models. But that is the whole point. An infinite variety of interpretations are possible for each basic unit, if that unit is a logical rather than a content idea. While the reader will see I enjoy interpreting these models my way, this will amount to five new interpretative theories out of, say, 50,000, in the sociological literature. But give me only 50 to 100 really distinct *logical* ideas about elementary social processes—and they are certainly in the literature now, merely obscured in content details—and I will bet they can be reinterpreted and recombined in the 50,000 ways that are necessary, I agree, to cope with social diversity.

Generalization of Structure

By 50 to 100 "really distinct" process ideas above, I imply most models are not so. Instead, they fall into *families*, each model in which is a variant of the same basic idea. Each of the chapters in this book is a particular variant of its family—a too particular variant—and dealing with each family as a whole is one of two major pieces of unfinished business on which I wish to conclude.

For example, consider Chapter 1. It postulates structural details that fit its main example, the survival of television programs. Those programs are seen as falling into separate types. Then a constant *fraction* of the remaining survivors of each type is eliminated each year. In other applications, it would be a constant *number* eliminated each period, linear rather than exponential decay; and instead of separate types, there could be a gradation, a continuous rather than discrete heterogeneity. And so on; there must be a dozen variants of value. One would need them all before he could speak of a "general" process here.

Fortunately, most variants probably exist already. If the simple algebra of Chapter 1 is translated into differential equations, it will link up with a whole family of "birth and death" processes in the mathematical literature. And survival processes where the rates of elimination are different at each stage, as in upward social mobility, will be enlightened by the Markov chain literature. So, when I speak of "standard" conceptual equipment I picture, say, a monograph containing *all* the variants—of survival processes, for example—of greatest probable use to sociologists.[22]

Another aspect to generalization is the question, would all variants lead to much the *same* general conclusions? Most would, but proving it is a sophisticated problem. It would require, for example, that the conclusions of Chapter 1 be shown to hold for *any* monotonic (never reversing) processes of decay. The enduring prize that such a general theorem becomes, is the reason that mathematical theorists, for example, in economics and portions of psychology, tend to shun computer simulation; but the whole point of the "modular" argument above is that the quarrel between the two is unnecessary. That they are not incompatible is being illustrated by a Social Science Research Council committee that is combining the best mathematical work in economic specialties into a joint computer model of the total economy.[23] I agree, however, that only when the conclusions have been generalized mathematically—freed of too particular details of logical structure—can we speak of "the" theory of such a situation.

Standardization of Method

The unfinished business that is *urgent*, however, is central to the "truth" issues surrounding these models (and the bigger systems that are configurations thereof). It is the need in sociology for a real sociometrics. Not Moreno's special meaning, but the standard meaning as in psychometrics and econometrics: an applied mathematical statistics, here of social process models. With the forthcoming publication of James S. Coleman's larger collection of models, Lee M. Wiggins', and others, including this program,[24] we are shortly going to have a whole new array of research tools, process measurement models, without the statistics to go with them.

For, the "truth" of these models boils down to statistical issues:

1. Is this the appropriate *model* for the situation?

2. If so, are the *parameters* characterizing that situation correctly estimated?

As to the first, I refuse to believe there are fixed truths in social affairs, and the truth of a model is a question of application. That is, we do not want to "reject" these models, but develop means of knowing *where* they apply. Yet I am convinced—as professionals would agree—that at least a half dozen models of any situation would pass the "tests" of fit that we as social scientists now apply, for example, some over-all chi square. More sophisticated tests will be needed which exploit the theory itself, for example, the subtle ways in which different variants would differ in (only) certain consequences. I do not pretend to begin that work in this book.

The other issue of truth is, of course, the one familiar in measurement: are the parameter values efficiently estimated? I carry that problem only a short halfway here. It is shown that every model can be solved for parameter estimates and that even these crude estimates do fit data. In other words, each model *can* be brought down to reality (or it is not in this book!); but with fallible data my algebraic solutions are not optimum uses of all the information. Until the latter are available, expert statistical advice is needed in any serious application.

NOTES

1. Allen Newell (ed.), *Information Processing Language*—V, The RAND Corporation, Englewood Cliffs, N.J.: Prentice-Hall, 1961.

2. I have not yet been able to try any of the three or four new simulation languages, but H. Markowitz's specifications are as if designed by social scientists. Inquiries may be made at the RAND Corporation, Santa Monica; but Simscript will probably be available through SHARE, the IBM users' group.

3. Arnold Toynbee argues convincingly that the social philosophers and historians have never been able to put it together either. Of all people, he also is interested in whether the logic machines can help. *New York Times*, Section 11, April 30, 1961.

4. "A Model for Analyzing Voting Systems," with Robert B. Smith, in *Public Opinion and Congressional Elections*, W. N. McPhee and W. A. Glaser, eds. New York: Free Press of Glencoe, 1962. A number of papers in that collection are inseparable from the five in this collection. Especially relevant are "Political Immunization" (with Jack Ferguson), a problem in the electoral dynamics discussed below, and "Attitude Consistency" (with Bo Anderson and Harry Milholland), Part III of which is a crucial extension of Chapter 4 here.

5. In a doctoral dissertation in sociology, Columbia University. Long-range prediction in economic demography is illustrated in Orcutt, Greenberger, Korbel, and Rivlin, *Microanalysis of Socio-Economic Systems: A Simulation Study* (New York: Harpers, 1961).

6. Let me exempt the simulation of psychological processes—of human thinking, for example—from all the following remarks about being "lost" in the implications of a theory, the need for mathematical analysis of what its components imply, and so on. Because of opposite location of the unobservables, the psychological complexity is at the level of elementary processes. Since these are unobservable, what is problematic about this work is *empirical*. As psychological models aggregate consequences, however, those consequences become simpler and simpler, until finally a familiar act like a human thought appears. Large social models are the opposite in every respect, for example, see the first reference in Note 12.

7. There are two difficulties. One is processing and analyzing the mountains of output from particular runs. This problem seems on its way to solution in the new languages like Markowitz's "Simscript," which take the work out of output reduction. The more serious problem is systematic exploration of the huge "parameter spaces" these big models entail. On this, I am optimistic that computer work in the linear-programming style will eventually permit one to make efficient explorations. An example of the latter that is close to social science problems is: Maas, Hufschmidt, Dorfman, Thomas, Marglin, and Fair, *Design of Water Resource Systems* (Cambridge, Mass.: Harvard University Press, 1962).

8. Richardson, L. W., M. Rashevsky and E. Trucco, eds., *Arms and Insecurity* (Chicago, Quadrangle Books, 1961).

9. I am much indebted at this point to the example of James S. Coleman's work with computers at Johns Hopkins.

10. See the many references in William Feller, *An Introduction to Probability and Its Applications* (second edition; New York: Wiley, 1957).

11. I grossly oversimplify the case with social theory generally (and with much of Parsons as well) because it *does* say much more than simply conceptualization alone, but much of this dynamic material with real deductive power (in potential) is not asserted formally *as* the theory, rather than as support for its categories, for example, as "reasons."

12. Plans to analyze it now are given in "Simulation Models: Analytic Variety and the Problem of Model Reduction," and the original model is F. E. Balderston and A. C. Hogatt, *The Simulation of Market Processes*, both Berkeley, Calif.: Management Science Research Group Working Papers, 1961 (the former) and 1960 (the latter).

13. Or if not subroutines, languages, for the computer languages referred to earlier are, under the surface, standard sub-routines, say, of 100–200 instructions each, which are called into operation by a brief symbol such as "Find ———."

14. Double thanks are due to Becker. Not only Chapter 3, but Chapter 1, "Survival Theory in Culture," owes its origins to the same concern with mass culture systems.

15. This is in the "media" model of the Simulmatics Corporation. The Simulmatics work by Pool and Robert Abelson for the Democrats in 1960 is *not* to be confused with the voting model in this book. Theirs used essentially statistical procedures like the Orcutt group's (Note 7), which are far more *responsible* than theoretical processes like those in this book, for prediction in immediate applications.

16. By Dr. Frank Scalora, Service Bureau Corporation, New York. A summary discussion will appear in the *Proceedings, Eighth Annual Convention*, N.Y., Advertising Research Foundation, Fall, 1962.

17. Thanks are due to Bertram M. Gross for background here.

18. An extensive bibliography is available from Allen Newell and Herbert A. Simon of The Graduate School of Industrial Administration, The Carnegie Institute of Technology, Pittsburgh.

19. Chapter 2 is left unformalized to illustrate the computer programming. Its "analysis" is therefore only illustrative.

20. An easily read review is W. S. Torgerson, *Theory and Method of Scaling* (New York: Wiley, 1960).

21. In Part III of McPhee, Anderson, and Milholland, "Attitude Consistency," cited in Note 4. That work was done, however, without knowledge of a maximum likelihood solution by Frederick Lord cited in Torgerson, Note 20.

22. I can think of no more useful thing for coming years than such monographs.

23. Inquiry should be made at the Council, 230 Park Avenue, New York.

24. Coleman's will be *Mathematics in Social Research* (New York: The Free Press of Glencoe, 1963). Wiggins' original work is in *Mathematical Models for the Interpretation of Attitude and Behavior Change*, New York Doctoral Dissertation in Sociology, Columbia University, 1955. As an example of others, the Stanford Sociology Department is editing a collection of formal models for release in 1963.

Survival Theory

in Culture

1

This paper[1] analyzes an old problem in culture that is becoming a new one in politics. It is the troublesome theory—and one trouble is that it has been a theory only in the sense of an argument or defense—that the "survival of the fittest" applies to culture. Creative ideas and aesthetics that meet the test of survival are supposed to be, if not the best, the most fitting for the people in question.

This argument is becoming the underlying ideological issue in the politics of mass culture. For what we have in that culture today, to defend or attack, is what has survived the tests of the

1. Funds for this work were drawn from a general grant to the writer, for models of social processes, by the Social Science Division of the National Science Foundation, NSF G# 13045. The problem developed from work with Professor Samuel Becker of the University of Iowa on a computer model of a typical mass culture system and from the request of Robert Hatch of *The Nation* for an analysis of the logical problems inherent in the television "ratings" problem. I am indebted to Anthony Oberschall for a solution to the two-class model.

box office, ratings, sales figures, and the like. One might say that the defense of that culture rests on Darwin, its criticism on Gresham. To oversimplify, the first argues that what has survived is for that reason the best the audience will accept, the second says, the worst.

Everyone appreciates that these are more slogans than analyses, of course. For example, if intellectuals mean seriously to argue from Gresham's law and similar analogies, such as the "lowest common denominator," their intellectual grounds are unclear. For in their own cultural fields they believe that survival is a sign of positive merit, and they have not explained clearly why it should be different in somebody else's field. Nor has the Gresham kind of alternative ever been given a precise meaning in culture. For when we attempt to make a logical model with the same assumptions about audiences that Gresham made about consumers, it strictly implies the opposite of its advocate's intent. In culture, it would not be the good but the bad that is driven out.[2]

Actually, it is as unnecessary as it is implausible to postulate that different survival theories apply to different cultures. For, mass culture is vulnerable on the grounds of its *own* defense, that the "Darwinian" test of survival as accepted in other fields applies here as well. For it is true that the idea that what survives is fitting can be rested on sensible assumptions that do fit the data of mass culture, but then the implications are anything but a defense of existing practices in that culture. Our main illustration will be a diagnosis of problems—and unexpected opportunities—found by fitting a model of the "Darwin" type to data on survival of television programs in the past decade.

If the usual theory of the test of survival applies to mass culture as well, but with unhappy results, why has it served us so

2. The Gresham model, it turns out, is not different from the Darwinian one we use in the subsequent text. The reason is that Gresham's traders and consumers were rational, as are the audiences (as best they can be) in this model. The mass culture discussion (and therefore mine) uses these terms only in layman's senses, as above.

well elsewhere—in literature, music, and science? A main purpose of this paper—which it would be unfortunate to lose sight of in its topical illustrations—is to present a formal theory of the difference between modern mass culture and traditional high and folk culture.

Most of us have assumed the different results in mass culture have their roots in one main problem, the mass audience and its tastes; but mass culture has also introduced changes in "the rules of the game," and a key one is a different way the survival process operates. This one difference, alone, accounts for the opposite results found in mass and high culture in such a thoroughgoing way that it may be quite unnecessary to postulate differences in the quality of the aesthetic responses of the people involved (for example, to assume that Shakespeare's audiences had better cultural instincts than our modern television audiences).

Indeed, television is interesting precisely because, with the same audience, it could be so much better than we would ever expect. Almost uniquely it combines the formal advantages of classic and folk culture with, unhappily, the self-defeating practices of mass culture. The missed opportunities that result from the latter, which can be calculated, will illustrate that mass culture's problems are rooted not just in taste but in logic.

The paper is addressed to nonmathematical readers, and pains are accordingly taken to explain the formulas and illustrate the implications concretely at all points. The argument *is*, however, logical—the whole idea is that some of these questions are not matters of opinion—so understanding some formal notation at the start will be essential to follow the sequel (where, then, formal details will be only for technical proof and can be skipped).

1. DEFINITIONS

The core problem in the theory of survival, as a test of merit, can be called "the wheat and chaff problem." In any kind of screening to eliminate chaff that we do not wish to survive, any process that eliminates chaff also loses wheat and any process that holds wheat also retains chaff—even when one can see which is chaff and which wheat. Yet even that identification is unclear in culture, as if a blind man were doing the screening. None of us knows nor agrees on, for example, how much "good" material is available in what we are offered, how much good material is being lost, and how much "chaff" is being retained instead.

This old problem is attacked here by giving these ambiguous and disputed quantities, for all that we can see them very roughly, the same technical status as *unobservables* in a scientific theory. We postulate that they exist and then connect them, algebraically, to the necessary consequences they would have in observed (here unambiguous and undisputed) data. In that way, one can solve for the former unknowns in terms of combinations of the latter observables.

For the unknowns, we use a notation made familiar by Hollywood, e.g. "B movies," with three such classes of material being the minimum necessary for analysis. Let

A = proportion of new cultural offerings each period which are of Class A.

B = proportion of new offerings which are Class B.

C = proportion of new offerings which are Class C.

$1.0 = A + B + C$ = "input" = total new offerings each period.

a = probability Class A offerings will survive one elimination, i.e., survive into the next period.

b = probability Class B will survive one elimination.

c = probability Class C will survive one elimination.

s_1 = total proportion of input that survives one elimination, i.e., the observed average probability of survival.

This notation becomes clear in the problem we will now consider, the algebraic definitions being located in Table 1a and corresponding numbers from a television example in Table 1b, which should be considered jointly.

Table 1a

Definitions in the Logical Model

	Survive	Do Not		
Class A	aA	$(1-a)A$	$=$	A
Class B	bB	$(1-b)B$	$=$	B
Class C	cC	$(1-c)C$	$=$	C
	s_1	$(1-s_1)$	1.0	$=$ input

Table 1b

Survival of New Television Offerings

	Survive	Do Not		
Class A	7	1	$=$	8
Class B	16	4	$=$	20
Class C	17	55	$=$	72
	40	60	100	$=$ input

Taking up the tables in inverse order, first note in the lower table an illustration of the quantities we would *like* to know, if they could be observed concretely. Out of every hundred new television programs, for example, how many are Class A, B, and C? And how many of each survive the test, for example, of their first season on the air? Actually, the numbers used in the illustration in Table 1b, except for a certain arbitrariness concerning the distinction between A and B discussed later, *are* actual estimates for recent years in television (averages for 1955–56 to 1960–61). For example, note how effective television seems to be, by these estimates, in screening out its chaff. About 55 out of about 72 of the Class C programs do not survive even one year; but note the estimate that 17 of these normally rejected programs do survive, a "chaff" error. And note that there is an opposite kind of error, a "wheat error," whereby five of the inevitably scarce A and B programs are estimated to be lost immediately, in their first season.

These estimates were not obtained, however, by aesthetic judgments. (Our language to that effect—that is, "Class C"—

expresses only what is the obvious intent of the people them-selves when they, for example, reject 55 out of 72 offerings.) In-stead of any such direct observation, the estimates were obtained as solutions satisfying a logical model of how corresponding un-knowns, defined in Table 1a, would relate to observable data.

The notation of Table 1a is essential. To repeat here: in the lower right, the sum of all new offerings in the period is set equal to 1.0. This is called the "input" and is the sum of subfractions of programs of different types. The names of the classes—A, B, or C—also stand for the *proportion* each is of the input of new offerings. The types differ only in that they have different proba-bilities of surviving subsequently. The proportions, a, b, and c of each, respectively, survive any one elimination. For example, if all the A material survived, that would be $1 \times A$ and thus $a = 1$; but in television only about .8 survive. Thus, the proportion .2, or $1 - a$, is lost; this loss will play a major role later. The sur-vivors of B and C proportions of material are defined analogously.

The sum of all survivors of one elimination, called s_1, is an example of an "observable"; that is, it can be determined unam-biguously that, say, 40 per cent of all new programs in a given year survive to the next year. It is related to the unknowns by the fact, for example, that if $s_1 = .40$, then

$$aA + bB + cC = s_1 = .40.$$

2. ASSUMPTIONS

We now make the following defining assumptions:

Whoever and whatever decide survival in the system express *their* idea of "better" by

$$a > b > c \tag{1}$$

but the problem is that, first, they do not fully know nor *agree:*

$$a \neq 1 \qquad c \neq 0 \tag{2}$$

and there is scarcity, among other reasons because people mean by better *unusually* so:

$$A < B < C \qquad (3)$$

The first assumption is merely that we agree to label the higher survival rate a and thus call what people let survive at a better rate Class A and what they often reject Class C. The second assumption says there is error in this, however—chaff retained and wheat lost. The third merely says the best material is scarcer than the worst. These are less assumptions than definitions of what the *problem* is.

What is controversial is only the heuristic suggestion of the first labeling. Intellectuals think it assumes that survival itself means "better." This is not so in the model. It itself will show why survivors would tend to be dominated by C material in much mass culture, by B material in television, and by A material in classical music. And in all three cases, intellectuals would dislike even more the bulk of what did not survive. (They should see the list of what did not survive long in television!) It is best to hold objections, then, because the problem is precisely to find out what it is that we are objecting to in some of these cultures.

Now define two fundamentally different kinds of systems: *single* screening and *repetitive* screening. The former has only one big test: new offerings this season are a "success" or they fail, and that settles it. A symbol of what we mean is when the opening-night reviews of a Broadway play settle the issue then and there. (In most cases, however, it takes some weeks or months, which we consider together as one testing period.) Then in single screening the next cycle—for example, next year—is a "new game" with virtually all new offerings. Even the previous successes last no more than one or two periods. Examples are the movies, popular music, and to a considerable degree best-selling books—in fact, most popular culture is of this transient type.

The single-screening pattern is formally defined as follows. If we let s_0 be the survivors before any elimination, s_1 the proportion of survivors after one season's elimination, and s_2 that after two eliminations, then the single screening system is simply

$$s_0 = A + B + C \; (= 1.0)$$
$$s_1 = aA + bB + cC \qquad\qquad (4)$$
$$s_2 = 0$$

This is what happens to *one* year's input in successive years. What would be the culture we would have, at a single time, from several years' input? Let S be the sum of all survivors at any one such time. In the single-screen case it is simply the present period's new input and last period's successful survivors, respectively, in the two parentheses of the upper row:

$$S = (A + B + C) + (aA + bB + cC)$$
$$= A(1 + a) + B(1 + b) + C(1 + c) \qquad (5)$$

The last row in expression (5) will be especially important in the sequel, because as the shorthand sum of the survivors at any time, it is the "culture" we have available in active use. It will, throughout, be what we compare with corresponding culture in the repetitive screening situation.

Turning to the latter, repetitive screening, note as one example that in television the survivors do not die out during the second season but compete all over again. The survivors of that elimination, in turn, do not retire but compete again in the next season. And so on. Actually, this kind of repetitive screening is seldom found in mass culture; it is instead the logical form of high culture and folk culture. For example, classical music must compete for performance over and over again, during the next year, the next decade, the next generation, and the next century. Different fields of repetitive culture would require slightly different assumptions, but we show the most general case (which also happens to fit television data). It is that the *same* elimination process is simply repeated over and over again, screening the survivors of the survivors, the survivors of those survivors, and so on, always under *identical* competitive conditions. The survivors after 0, 1, 2, . . . , n eliminations, the remaining fractions of the original input, $s_1, s_2, \ldots, s_n$, would be

$$s_0 = A + B + C \ (= 1.0)$$
$$s_1 = aA + bB + cC$$
$$s_2 = a(aA) + b(bB) + c(cC) = a^2A + b^2B + c^2C$$
$$\cdot$$
$$\cdot \qquad\qquad (6)$$
$$\cdot$$
$$s_n = a^nA + b^nB + c^nC$$

That is, if we always take the proportion, a, of the proportion a that survives before, the sequence is $a, a^2, a^3, a^4, \ldots$. (Since a is less than 1, a fraction, squaring and cubing it of course diminishes survival.)

Expression (6) above shows the fate of only *one* batch of offerings through subsequent years—the fractions surviving at each time, $s_1, s_2, \ldots, s_n$. But we want the sum, S, of all the survivors of different inputs still active in the culture at any one moment. If the same conditions had been repeated for n periods, then S would be the sum of all the remaining survivors of n different batches of offerings put in at different times and thus in n different stages of elimination now. The different batches are shown in parentheses below, from the newest on the left to the survivors of the oldest on the right:

$$S = (A + B + C) + (aA + bB + cC) + (a^2A + b^2B + c^2C)$$
$$+ \cdots + (a^nA + b^nB + c^nC)$$

The string of algebraic terms would become large as years were added, but the oldest material would become negligible and mortality all down the line would finally balance input. That is, S goes to a limit. This can be shown to be:

$$S \rightarrow \frac{A}{1 - a} + \frac{B}{1 - b} + \frac{C}{1 - c} \qquad\qquad (7)$$

where n is large. For the terms in the earlier expression can be arranged so that we consider only, say, all A material alone. Its sum still surviving is the sum of a geometric series, $A + aA + a^2A + \cdots$, whose limiting sum can be shown to be $A/(1 - a)$. This is the amount of Class A material we can expect to have in the active "steady state," where losses of A material finally balance input of A material. This sum is expressed in units of annual input $= 1.0$ (which in television, for example, is around 50 new nighttime programs each season). An expression like $A/(1 - a)$ could be very sizable indeed, if $1 - a$ were small (which means if we *held* the A material well). Analogous reasoning applies to B and C material. The sum of these limiting sums in expression (7) above is the "culture" active at any one time in the repetitive system, comparable to expression (5) earlier for the single-screening case.

3. THE TELEVISION EXAMPLE

Before we go on to analyze what these expressions imply, it is useful to digress in order to make the symbols concrete with illustrative data from television. For instance, rough averages in recent years for television have been $C = .7, c = .2$, $A + B = .3$ and $a = .8, b = .8$. An appended Technical Note shows how these estimates were obtained. The equations of the repetitive model were solved for the unknowns (hereafter called "parameters"), yielding formulas by which they can be calculated from knowns, such as the average longevity of programs, annual replacement needs, and especially the observed survival fractions, $s_1, s_2, \ldots, s_n$. This was done for each year's input of new *nighttime* television programs in the 1950s, and the data are also given in the appended Technical Note.[3] The resulting parameters for

3. The data were collected by Florence McClure, to whom special thanks are due, from Nielson reports kindly made available by Thomas Coffin, Director of Research, and Paul Hiromura, ratings specialist, of the National Broadcasting Company. The universe consists of programs on from

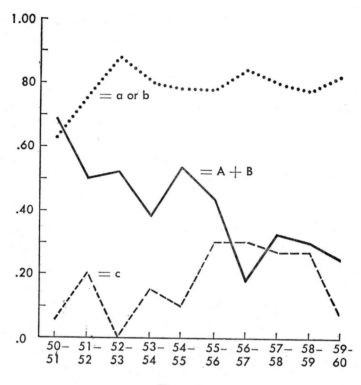

Figure 1

Estimated parameters for programs originating in 1950–51 through 1959–60.

television have not been constant over time, but varied from year to year roughly as shown in Figure 1.

The parameters A, a, etc., attach not to the active culture, S, at any one time, but to a batch of new programs all put in at the same time, like an age group or age cohort. These dates of *origin* of the programs are the manner of classification along the hori-

---

7:30 to 11:00 P.M. EST, excluding news and *ad hoc* programs like specials. The "season" was defined as *any* of four weeks, the first two in November or the last two in February, a program not appearing in *any* of these not being considered to have appeared regularly this year.

zontal. The verticals are, first, the proportion of A and B material in that input at that time of origin. Then a, b, and c for that given year's input characterize its annual survival rates *thereafter*.

For example, the lowest line is the probability, c, that Class C material in that year's input of programs would survive any single subsequent elimination (season). The top line stands for either a or b, since, as discussed later, the survival rates of A and B material in television are indistinguishable (that is, $a = b$). As Figure 1 shows, however, there is a sharp discrimination (large difference) in survival rates between a or b and c. Similarly, the solutions for the case of television cannot distinguish between A and B input, because they do not survive differently (that is, television itself does not make the distinction). But we know their sum and the remainder of the input, C material. The $A + B$ sum is shown, with the vertical difference between that and the top of the chart being the fraction of input in each year of Class C.

One must be careful, however, about interpretation of the drastic change in $A + B$ versus C after 1955. Observed survival rates in television were definitely lower for programs put in after 1955, with finally only a quarter of the programs originating in 1959–60 surviving even to the next season, 1960–61. The model's solution's interpret this weakening of survival as due to weaker input, less new A and B material and much more C. Strictly speaking, however, the latter means *short-lived* material, *not* necessarily "C aesthetics." Moreover, the change coincides closely with increasingly effective competition from the third network, the American Broadcasting Company, beginning in the mid-1950's and producing a three-way contest for top leadership by 1960. This is an aspect of noncomparability in competition (although the total number of programs presented at night, our universe, has not changed) that would lower survival rates.

If tougher competition is the cause, however, then the model says its effect is peculiar. Much more *new* material is meeting an *early* demise, the technical meaning of increased C, whereas the remaining older material and the durable fraction of the new material are *un*affected (*a* and *b* unchanged). These results would be consistent with an interpretation that the new Hollywood input, which also increased sharply after about 1955, contained a higher proportion of transient material. The writer's guess is that something else is at the root of the problem: that replacing the talent and idea resources "used up" in the early heyday of television with anything as durable now is proving difficult for reasons discussed later. Whatever the cause, the prominence of short-lived material in recent years has the effect of shifting more of television toward the *single*-screen mode of processing transient material. While television does that kind of screening very well (*b* − *c* discrimination remains high), we shall see this is not putting its best foot forward.

How does one know these unobservables are as estimated? He cannot be certain. One can judge only from the fit of data generated by the model to real data. For example, $aA + bB + cC$ should equal the observed s_1, and so on. One can calculate the theoretic counterpart of $s_2, s_3, \ldots, s_n$. Table 2 shows the error that results when this is done and is then compared with real data. An error of .02 is about one program .04 two programs, and so on, comparing the number surviving (s_i) in a year with

Table 2

Instances of Error in Predicting s_i When There Are n s_i's to Predict with Three Parameters

Error:	.00 .01	.02 .03	.04 .05	.06 .07	.08 .09	.10 more
n						
4 or 5	6	2	1	—	—	—
6 or 7	3	1	4	2	2	1
8, 9, 10	8	11	3	2	2	1
	17	14	7	4	4	2

NOTE: The table entry is the number of instances of a given error when an instance is, for example, the comparison between the proportion of programs put in in 1950–51 that were still surviving in 1955–56 with that predicted by $s_5 = a^5A + b^5B + c^5C$ (where c, C, $A = B$, and $a = b$ were based on the 1950–51 input's survival for all subsequent years to 1960–61).

predictions for that batch of programs that year. Forty-eight such comparisons can be made for 1950 to 1960–61 in which the model would *not* fit exactly by definition, and these are what are shown (that is, the error in all other instances in the decade, not shown, is zero).

The fit is satisfactory, and the residual of error shown here could be reduced substantially by more efficient parameter estimates and averaging to obtain greater samples, if it were worth it.[4] It is not, for there is *direct* evidence below that these are the fitting assumptions for the case of television, as far as they go; and we wish to dwell instead on the general principles of the problem applying to many other fields where detailed data would surely not be fitted so well, but where the general principles would still apply.

There are five such general rules implied by the model, each a different cultural lesson, although they are not all distinct theorems mathematically. They are discussed below under the headings "repetition," "vulnerability," "discrimination," "size," and "interaction."

4. THE REPETITION PRINCIPLE

Note a main feature of modern mass culture, its "overnight success," or "hit," pattern. That is, there is emphasis on short-lived material that, if it passes one big test, enjoys its popularity almost all at once. Then, consumed by the available audience, it is not reconsidered again. Yesterday's popular music, for example, is gone today. Equate this with the *single* screening system.

Next, note the contrasting flavor of both high culture and folk culture, their "classic" or "traditional" flavor. That is, there

4. See the discussion at the end of the Technical Note of the need for more efficient estimates of a and b than the simple averaging procedure we used. The data would pass tests of fit, but the errors are not independent; instead, they are typically due to a bad parameter estimate being off "all down the line," that is, $s_1, s_2 \ldots , s_n$, all in error for the same reason.

is emphasis on long-lived material that has stood the repeated tests of time, and thus on a repertory chiefly accumulated from the past. Equate this with the *repetitive* screening system.

There are exceptions, it is true, both ways. Classic culture does not have a "patent" on the repetitive logic, and it is significant that popular music is often good when it is handled repetitively, namely, when it is yesterday's jazz. And by the same token, literature is often bad when it is single-screened, namely today's best sellers. But speaking generally, a program to analyze the consequences of mass culture's departure from classic culture's logic is to analyze how single and repetitive systems behave differently.

To recall, the sum of the active or surviving culture, S, was for each:

Single culture:

$$S = A(1 + a) + B(1 + b) + C(1 + c) \qquad (5)$$

Repetitive culture:

$$S = \frac{A}{1 - a} + \frac{B}{1 - b} + \frac{C}{1 - c} \qquad (7)$$

in which all terms are expressed in units of annual input, which we assume the same for each system in size and quality. Given other things equal in this manner, the first general proposition is simple: the repetitive system is *better*.

By "better" is meant what was assumed in expression (1) at the start, that the people in the system express their idea of "better" by allowing a high proportion of A material but not C to remain in the final culture. (We leave B alone, to pay the bills.) To see how much A material survives versus C material, the above expressions can be rearranged as the inequalities:

	Single	*Repetitive*
A material:	$A(1 + a) \neq$	$\dfrac{A}{1 - a}$
C material:	$C(1 + c) \neq$	$\dfrac{C}{1 - c}$

If we divide each inequality by its term in brackets on the left, they become

$$A \ll \frac{A}{1 - a^2} \tag{8}$$

$$C \lesssim \frac{C}{1 - c^2} \tag{9}$$

where we use the notation $\gg$ for "much greater than" and $\gtrsim$ for "not greatly different from." The reason will be apparent to the technical reader when he recalls that $a > b > 0$. Thus, expressions of the general form $A/(1 - a)$ tend toward a limit of $A/(1 - 1) = \infty$, while expressions of the general form $C/(1 - c)$ tend toward a limit of $C/(1 - 0) = C$.

What it means culturally is that:

A. The repetitive system accumulates more *good* material (because it "saves it up" over many periods, the single system only over one or two).

C. But it does not accumulate much more *bad* material (because the repetitive case "corrects its errors" by repeating testing, i.e., the probability, $c^2 \to 0$).

The advantage of the repetitive kind of system is only moderately greater, however, when it is not *exploited* properly. To illustrate, take the average parameters for television in the last half of the 1950s, $C = .72$, $c = .24$, and $b = a = .81$. Then, for illustration add the assumption we have had to make throughout and will justify later, that 5 to 10 per cent of television programs *should* be treated as A material. (We use 8 per cent, or about four or five A programs out of 50 to 60 new nighttime programs tried each year.) Then with these real parameters, Table 3 calculates what television would look like under three conditions: first as a single screening system, then as it is now, and finally as it could be if it exploited the repetitive logic better (namely, to change only one parameter from $a = .81$ to $a = .96$, which corresponds to television's holding its very best for a generation, as it has Jack Benny).

Table 3

Television's Surviving Culture, *S*, with Existing Parameters under Three Different Conditions

1. As a single-screening system (television parameters in expression 5)

A	*B*	*C*	*S*
10*	26	64	= 100 per cent

2. As it is *now* (repetitive, television parameters in expression 7)

A	*B*	*C*	*S*
17	44	39	= 100 per cent

3. As it *could* be (only change: $a = .96$ in expression 7)

A	*B*	*C*	*S*
50	26	24	= 100 per cent

* The table entry is the proportion that *A*, *B*, and *C* material, respectively, would be of the total surviving culture in active use, when existing television parameters are used: $C = .72$, $c = .24$, $B = .20$, $b = .81$, $A = .08$ and $a = .81$ in the first two cases, .96 in the third.

The main point of Table 3 is reflected in the off-diagonal, from upper right to lower left. The point is that as a single system, television would be dominated by Class *C* material. This is in contrast to the *B* material that is in the plurality now when television operates as an (inefficient) repetitive system and to the *A* material that could be in the *majority* with the same input and everything else the same, except one parameter change to exploit the repetitive logic better, whose feasibility for television is discussed later.

The differences involved are illustrated by the history of our native (popular) music. It has developed from a situation logically better than the third case in Table 3 above, two centuries ago (as folk music), to a situation perhaps like the second case in the table two decades ago (as swing and jazz), to one like the first case now (as completely transient material). Those who think there is nothing wrong with mass culture that improving tastes would not cure should try a few calculations like these themselves.

5. THE VULNERABILITY RULE

The second general principle the model reveals is this: single screening is vulnerable to letting the chaff in, repetitive screening to losing the wheat.

More precisely, the following is what can be proved:

In a single-screening culture, the immediate rate of change is always greater, and the maximum improvement usually greater, from a change in c, or "chaff," errors than in $1 - a$, or "wheat" errors.

In contrast, in a repetitive screening culture, the immediate rate of change is usually greater and the maximum improvement always greater, from a change in $1 - a$, or "wheat" errors than in c, or "chaff" errors.

Let the sum of the A material active in the surviving culture at any time be S_A and the corresponding sum of C material be S_C. Assume that the quality of this culture is helped as much by purging the latter as by fostering the former, that is, that a good index of quality is $S_A - S_C$. And let the "rate of improvement" consisting of increases in the former be δS_A (where we use lower-case delta, δ, for small changes, upper-case Δ for large changes). And let the "rate of deterioration" consisting of increases in the C material be δS_C. How these quantities change with change in a or c is denoted by, for example $\delta S_A/\delta a$ (the change in A with an increase in a or decrease in $1 - a$, that is, the partial derivative). These changes are

	Wheat-error *change*	*Chaff-error* *change*	
Single system:	$\dfrac{\delta S_A}{\delta a} = A$	$\dfrac{\delta S_C}{\delta c} = C$	(10)
Repetitive system:	$\dfrac{\delta S_A}{\delta a} = \dfrac{A}{(1 - a)^2}$	$\dfrac{\delta S_C}{\delta c} = \dfrac{C}{(1 - c)^2}$	(11)

In the top row, the right side would always be larger and thus a single system always more sensitive to changes in the *chaff* errors. Indeed expression (10) itself explains why. For, recall that $C \gg A$. Expression (10) shows C is the penalty or reward from changes in chaff errors, and thus they hurt most. It is worst, in other words, to relax one's guard where the numerical magnitudes are large, in the C case.

Quite contrary to intuition, however, this is *not* the case in the repetitive system, where errors involving the numerically large C input usually are not nearly so costly to long-run quality as are errors involving the numerically small (at input) A material. First, note that

$$\frac{1}{(1-a)^2} \gg \frac{1}{(1-c)^2}$$

For example, in television this ratio is about 27.7 to 1.7. The left is the controlling denominator term in change due to changes in a, which is why we say the repetitive system is "usually" most sensitive to "wheat" errors. It is true, however, that these terms are weighted by A and C, respectively, in the whole rates of improvement or deterioration in expression (11) above. It is therefore conceivable that input could be so bad (for example, worse than the ratio $A = 1.7$ to $C = 27.7$) that a repetitive system could temporarily be improved more from cutting down on chaff errors, as in the single system. But we shall see that this would only be a temporary expedient. For the maximum potential improvement considered in the next section will come, always in a repetitive system, from the correction of $1 - a$, or wheat, errors—that is, not losing the good material.

What it all means culturally is this: the single screening systems typical of mass culture are always on the *defensive* against the numerically large chaff that otherwise overwhelms the numerically small wheat, whereas a repetitive system is itself a natural or automatic defense against chaff. It corrects its chaff errors naturally the next time around. Rather the repetitive pathology is that it *repeats wheat errors*. They cumulate as an attrition precisely where otherwise a repetitive system's whole potential is, in its capacity to carry over the best from the past.

And here lies a contemporary, and let us hope temporary, tragedy in television. Recall that, technically, it is a repetitive system and, as such, is vulnerable to losing wheat. Television's intellectual critics instead focus on its chaff, it is true, and chaff trouble has been the visible symptom in recent years. Yet those who lived through it in the industry in the 1950s would surely agree that then the problem was losing wheat, "using up material." The model's diagnosis is that the latter is, indeed, the underlying difficulty.

This is illustrated by the calculations of Table 4. First, we always know the actual number of programs put into nighttime television every year (using the 1949–50 schedule as the "input" for the first year). And from the model's solution's one can roughly estimate how many of these new program series were A and B types—that is, potentially durable. The number of these estimated to have been created in a decade is impressive: more than 300 durable program series! One can just as easily calculate how many of them were *lost* each year, however, using the decade's average of $a = b = .8$, or .2 lost. The twenty-odd casualties a year among these better programs do not strike home until we cumulate these losses and compare the cumulative loss with the number of A and B programs still in use on the air. The comparison is striking: by the end of the decade, television had lost more than *three* times as many of these, its most durable and best programs, as remained on the air!

We label this loss the "drain" on resources, to introduce some conjectural calculations on the right of Table 4. (These are separated from the other estimates to indicate that this conjecture should not be confused with the other real estimates.) In the right column, a formal notion like "running out of ideas" is presented. Suppose television had been drawing on some "natural resources," original idea resources and talent reserves, R_1 (includ-

Table 4

Estimated Flow of *A* and *B* Programs In and Out of Nighttime Television, When *a* = *b* = 0.8 and *A* + *B* in Raw Programs = (*A* + *B*) (Actual Programs Input)

Year	Input, Raw No. $A + B$ Programs	Loss, 0.2 of $A + B$ on Air	In Use, Remain after Losses	"Drain," Cumulative Losses	"Reserves," Speculative R_t (See Text)
49–50[c]	67	13	54	13	137[b]
50–51	53	22	85	35	84
51–52	31	23	93	58	45
52–53	23	24	92	82	28
53–54	19	22	89	104	19
54–55	29	23	95	127	14
55–56	17	23	89	150	−1
56–57	6	20	75	170	−4
57–58	18	19	74	189	4
58–59	15	18	71	207	0
59–60	13	16	68	223	−1
60–61	14[a]	16	66	239	0

a. Average, previous five years.

b. Calculated from $R_1 = 137$, where R is before the input of the period, and $\Delta R = 14$, where ΔR is accrued during the period and available next period. Thus, 137 minus input of 67 plus ΔR of 14 is 84.

c. The whole 1949–50 schedule of which 67 programs were estimated to be *A* or *B*, is taken as the "initial" input.

ing, for example, the carryover of ideas and talents from radio). And suppose these resources were increased each year subsequently by a constant, ΔR, the "natural increment" due to new invention and new growth. The status of this resource or reserve at any subsequent time t would be

$$R_t = R_1 + t(\Delta R) - (\text{in use})_t - (\text{cumulative loss})_t \quad (12)$$

where the subtractions from the reserve denoted by the right terms are the programs on the air or previously (cumulatively) lost as in Table 4. Now suppose a system uses up ideas and talents too prolifically, faster than the natural growth rate by which it can invent new ones. Then it would exhaust some previously "unseen limits" on the number of ideas and talents that

are available in and to any one generation. Exhausting such resources would be signaled by a sharp drop in input of durable
material, later leveling off at some much lower but new constant
level, corresponding to ΔR. This is "living (only) on income,"
that is, on the much slower natural growth of new ideas and
talents, after the heritage is gone.

With these assumptions, expression (12) can be solved as
$R_1 = 137$, an original heritage of the wherewithal to create about
137 durable A and B nighttime program series. This is about the
size of all nighttime network radio. But $\Delta R = 14$, an annual re-
freshment of ideas and talents sufficient for creating only about
14 new durable (A or B) programs a year, by wholly current
invention.

The day of reckoning when the former heritage was gone and
now television had to live by the latter annual growth alone, by
these calculations, was about 1955–56. Note the different story
in input beyond that point, the space in Table 4.

For what it is worth, this is the writer's conjecture as to why
there has evidently been an increase since 1955–56 of the C type
input (that is to say, material that does not prove durable by
television's own standards). This transient material is not itself
the primary problem, but replacement needed because of what
was (and still is) that problem: the system's excessive loss, or
"using up," of better material faster than can be replaced now.
The symptom is chaff in the bread, but the diagnosis is that the
wheat was lost.

6. THE DISCRIMINATION PRINCIPLE

Returning to the general distinctions between single and
repetitive systems—and thus to what most mass culture is doing
that departs from the traditional logic of high and folk culture—
we consider now a discrimination idea. One could concentrate his
energies on a kind of "high discrimination," giving Class A material much better survival chances than Class B material in this

model; that is, one could concentrate upon retaining the *best* as opposed to the "not quite so good." Or one could concentrate his energies on "low discrimination," making a sharp distinction between B and C material in this model; that is to say, one could concencentrate on rejecting the *worst* as opposed to the "not so bad."

In that choice, the rule is that in a single-screening system it pays to discriminate low, between B and C; in a repetitive system it pays to discriminate high, between A and B.

More precisely, what can be proved is that:

In a single system, the immediate rate of return is always greater and the maximum return is usually greater, from increasing the difference $b - c$ than from increasing $a - b$.

In a repetitive system, the immediate rate of return is usually greater and the maximum return is always greater, from increasing the difference $a - b$ than from increasing $b - c$.

First, consider the immediate *rate* of return. To increase the difference $a - b$ is the same as increasing a and decreasing b. To increase the difference $b - c$ is to increase b and decrease c. Class B material changes at the same rate in each case, with simply opposite signs; and unless one has some special preference for adding to or ridding himself of B material, the different return from each strategy would depend on changing a versus changing c. In other words, there is a choice, in achieving the better discrimination we are concerned with here, between reducing "wheat errors" or "chaff errors." So, the formal argument on discrimination is the same as that on vulnerability in the last section: namely, that the rate of improvement is always greater in a single system from improved rejection of C material—from $b - c$ discrimination—whereas the rate of return is usually greater in a repetitive system from improved retention of A material—from $a - b$ discrimination.

As for the *maximum* potentials, which we deferred considering in the last section, where they apply as well, the maximum improvement in retention of A is up to $a = 1$ and the maximum improvement in rejection of C is down to $c = 0$. If one could achieve anything like these maximum potentials, the effects would be, respectively,

	Single system	Repetitive system	
Change a:	$\operatorname*{Max}_{a \to 1} \Delta S_A = +A(1 - a)$	$+ \infty A$	(13)
Change c:	$\operatorname*{Max}_{c \to 0} \Delta S_C = -C(c)$	$-C\left(\dfrac{c}{1 - c}\right)$	(14)

The right column is now the repetitive case, and that case is easily dispatched. The maximum return from $a - b$ or "high" discrimination is when a goes to 1 and that implies, by the notation $+ \infty$, that Class A material can grow over all bounds. For if $1 - a$ errors go to zero, that means the best material adds cumulatively over all time. This has been the essential secret of the development of fields like mathematics and science, where the input of first-rate creation has been small in most past generations, but practically none of it has been lost. If so, what does it matter for the quality of science today that it was not always careful about the other kind of discrimination, between usable ideas and outright fallacies? What matters in a repetitive system is recognizing the best, not the worst.

The contrary argument in the single case, that what pays is discrimination on the low side between usable material and outright chaff, is always true of the rate of return but is now only "usually" true when we consider maximums. For, it could be that "wheat errors" are so large that $(1 - a)/c > C/A$. This is a rare possibility, but logic agrees with common sense that then it is possible that there could be larger maximum return from improving high discrimination so as to retain A material (even though the *rate* of return therefrom is always smaller). This possibility could also arise when good material is especially plentiful in a single system, that is, when $A \approx C$, or when discrimination against bad material is already severe, that is, when $c \approx 0$. The Broadway theater, for example, borders on all of these conditions, which the reader might note for later discussion of Broadway's "carrying good logic too far." Aside from these rare combinations affecting maximum prospects, the best policy in a single system is "low" discrimination, between B and C material.

The major American magazines illustrate good single-screening strategy, probably bordering on $b = a$, but with $c \approx 0$—that is, not exclusiveness but sharp low discrimination against incompetence. This good policy for single-screening, however, goes awry when applied to a repetitive system—namely, television. As estimated earlier, there $a = b = .8$ and c is about .2, which means virtually *no* discrimination between A and B material but sharp discrimination between B and C material. Television does not "discriminate between its successes" but only between them and its failures. It is shown above that this is the opposite of good logic in a repetitive system, so that it is important to say how we *know* that television fails to make the high discrimination.

Technically, this conclusion turns up as a failure to find any significant A in solutions,[5] but it is apparent to anyone in raw data as follows. Figure 2 shows what the observed survival rates would look like for a repetitive system that really was treating three different classes of material distinctly, that is, $a \neq b \neq c$. The survival of a batch of offerings over time would be a deeply concave curve at first, then level out after there was nothing left but A material to a "flat" curve of perpetuation of that material.

Now, what television data actually look like (data are shown in the Technical Note) is as if the bottom portion of Figure 2

5. For varied input years, either A comes out negative and about zero, or a small positive number like the two programs of the 129 in the 1949–50 input that are now behaving as if $1 = a > b$, namely, "What's My Line?" and "The Ed Sullivan Show." Probably there *is* an A category in television, in these programs, and in Jack Benny, but it is too small to be picked up in solutions as significantly different from zero.

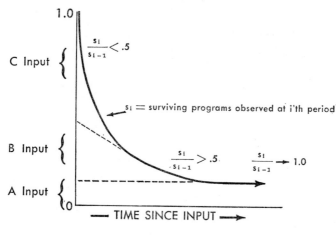

Figure 2

How survival rates would look with three distinct classes. The example shown is $a = 1$.

were eliminated. In television, the point where B material is gone and survival "levels off" is at virtually zero survival of everything! We do not think this means "there is no A material" in television input. Rather, what is there is not *treated* differently from B material. Since the latter erodes at a rate much too high for first-rate material, with about 20 per cent of the previous survivors dying each and every year, at the end of a decade virtually everything is gone. Only two programs, for example, remain from the 129 in the 1949–50 nighttime schedule.

Next, note in Figure 2 references to a ratio, s_i/s_{i-1}. This ratio means the proportion of the previous survivors that survive again. In a system that is discriminating between material differentially, this ratio will keep increasing—with the passage of time. As the culture is "purified" by successive screening, what remains will be better able to survive. Table 5 shows the behavior of this ratio over time for television programs.

In television, the ratio increases after the first period, signifying that the transient C material is being purged and that the

Table 5

Proportion of Survivors after Elimination $i - 1$ Who Survive Elimination i

s_i/s_{i-1} when $i =$

Time of Input	1	2	3	4	5	6	7	8	9	10	11
1949–50 schedule as input with $i = 0$ in 49–50:	.45	.81	.66	.84	.73	.74	.79	.73	$\frac{3}{8}$	$\frac{2}{3}$	$\frac{2}{2}$[a]
Average for input in 50–51 thru 54–55:	.47	.70	.72	.79	.75	.69	.92	.67	$\frac{7}{8}$	$\frac{3}{4}$	
Average for input in 55–56 thru 59–60:	.38	.58	.64	$\frac{5}{5}$							

a. Raw programs shown where N is less than 10. See Technical Note for original data.

$A + B$ that remains can now stand successive tests better. Next, among the initial successes, if A versus B material subsequently survived differently, in due time the ratio would *again* increase as the B programs dropped out. Until finally, when all that remained was A, the ratio s/s_{i-1} would approach 1 or at least some $a > b = .8$. This does not happen dependably in television. Instead, what television picks to survive, that is to say, what would be A, survives no better than did what it picked *from* in the preceding year, that is, including B. We have to conclude that television cannot make the A versus B discrimination and instead treats both with rates appropriate to B material, namely, the large losses that prevent television from retaining virtually anything from, say, the previous decade.

The penalty can be calculated in an interesting way. Any text on probability will show that the term on the left in the following equation is the expected lifetime,[6] in periods, of material with

6. This is the *mean* survival; that is, some A programs would be lost immediately and some lost in 40 years, but the mean of the distribution by longevity would be $a/(1 - a)$. See William Feller, *Introduction to Probability*, Second Edition (New York: Wiley, 1957), p. 210, where Feller's number of failures preceding first success is our number of successes preceding first failure.

probability a of surviving and $1 - a$ of not surviving in any one period:

$$\frac{a}{1 - a} + 1 = \frac{1}{1 - a} = \frac{A}{1 - a}\left(\frac{1}{A}\right) \qquad (15)$$

Note the center term for later reference. It is a short expression for the terms on the far right. They provide a new unit for measuring the amount of A material expected in the final culture, which was $A/1 - a$ in units of total annual input. But total annual input is $1/A$ times as great as, or $1/A$ multiples of, the annual input of A material alone. So, on the far right above, $(A/1 - a)1/A$ is the A material expected in the final culture now expressed in multiples of the annual input of A material (alone).

Therefore, what the far left and far right terms in expression (15) above imply is

Expected life of A programs $+ 1$
  $=$ multiples of the A fraction of input in the final culture

Thus, the capacity of the repetitive system to accumulate large multiples of the average input for single years—its essential advantage over the single system—is not just "a function of" but *is* the longevity it accords to that A material.

Now consider the cost of a missed opportunity. Instead of letting its best, the potential A material, die out or wear out as quickly as its B material, with 20 per cent lost every year, suppose television let some significant class of A programs survive, say, an average of a generation. (The latter average would still mean about 4 per cent a year lost, or $1 - a = .04$.) The different effect on the multiples of A material surviving for use at any time would contrast with the current case as follows:

Television as it is now:

$$\frac{a}{1 - a} + 1 = \frac{.8}{.2} + 1 = 5 \text{ multiples of } A \text{ in use at any time}$$

If A survived a generation (average):

$$\frac{a}{1-a} + 1 = \frac{.96}{.04} + 1 = 25 \text{ multiples of } A \text{ in use at any time}$$

The cost of not making the A versus B discrimination, then, is as much as $25 - 5 = 20$ multiples of the best programs television can invent in any one year. And here lies, we think, a main defect in the "ratings" system. For, ratings (and sponsor) make the *low* discrimination, between durable B material and rapid C failures, but in the nature of the case cannot "discriminate between successes," to make the high discrimination necessary to build up A without a self-defeating buildup of B as well.

But does television have any "A material"? It is better to ask: how much material *should* television treat as A, whether it "is" or not? Recall the expected amount of A material in the final culture is $A/(1-a)$. About the smallest one could make the denominator in that expression is .04, the expected lifespan of 25 years above, with .04 annual loss due to deaths of talent and generational changes of taste. If so, the smallest we can make the numerator, A, and still have A material at least 50 per cent of the surviving repertory at all times, is $A = .08$ with other television parameters as they are now. So, somewhere around 8 to 10 per cent of the entrants into competition for survival in prime time—say, the best one-tenth of what Hollywood and New York together can offer—should be preserved from wearing out and dying out, as the minimum we *have* to accept as A to prevent the majority of the surviving culture from being, as it would otherwise, still *worse* B and C material. Snobs who deny there "is" any A worth preserving in television, then, are asking for something worse.

7. THE SIZE RULE

Yet now consider this contradiction. The old broadcasting did hold onto its best material; for example, the top programs changed little from the late 1930s to the late 1940s. But then there was trouble getting room for *new* ideas on the air, and thus the discovery of better material that is necessary at all times was inhibited. Opera today is encountering a similar difficulty. The *A* material from the nineteenth century and before is being held so well that the repertory has little "room" to encourage fresh creation. Does this mean that the classic logic of repetitive systems—not to lose the best of the past—is the antithesis of fresh creation?

Not so. The problem that broadcasting and opera illustrate, instead, is the effect of an arbitrary ceiling on the *size* of a culture. A fixed size, a limited television schedule or a small opera repertory, is self-defeating in a repetitive system. Whereas, restriction of size is just what the doctor ordered—but mass culture did not listen—for a single-screening system.

The general rule is: size and quality are negatively correlated in a single system, positively correlated in a repetitive system. Specifically, what can be proved is that, with a fixed input:

Quality is improved in a single system by decreasing over-all survival rates down to an optimum size of the surviving culture *smaller* than is practically feasible.

Quality is improved in a repetitive system by increasing over-all survival rates up to an optimum size of the surviving culture *larger* than is practically feasible.

Recall that "quality" is what the people in the system themselves find to be durable, to stand the test of use, namely, the more *A* and the less *C* in the surviving culture, the better for them. So, again let us say an index of quality is $S_A - S_C$. Next, increasing and decreasing "over-all" survival rates can be represented by $\Delta a = \Delta b = \Delta c$. For, one cannot clamp down by making survival more difficult without losing good material as well, nor assure survival by making criticism more lenient without retaining bad material as well. Then the question becomes: In what direction and at what magnitude would an over-all change, $\Delta a = \Delta b = \Delta c$, result in optimum quality?

The optimum direction of change is already answered by the partial derivatives of—the rates of improvement from—changes in a and c. For example, in a single system the return from a change in a is in proportion A and from a change in c in proportion C. Now, if both rates changed the same amount, then we would *not* wish to go "up," for that would mean to gain only in proportion $+A$ at the much larger cost in proportion $+C$. To go "down," to lose in proportion $-A$ but with larger benefit in proportion $-C$, would be what would pay off in the single case.

The derivatives in the repetitive case had the opposite and nonintuitive import: we would want to go "up." Namely, the return from a change in a was in proportion $A/(1 - a)^2$ and from a change in proportion $C/(1 - c)^2$. Now, the latter would usually be much smaller, but could give a larger return in rare cases. Yet even then the return would soon exhaust itself, as $c \to 0$, and then one would discover the *optimum* point had been in the opposite direction, the $+\Delta a$ change having the real potentials. For the optimums in over-all change are

	Optimum over-all change is $\Delta a = \Delta b = \Delta c =$	With consequence that $S_A =$	$S_C =$	
Single:	$-c$	$A(1 + a - c)$	0	(16)
Repetitive:	$+(1 - a)$	$+\infty$	$\dfrac{C}{a - c}$	(17)

There is nothing really new mathematically here, but a practical result that is not intuitive to us as practical men. First, to achieve the above optimums would in principle violate our assumptions of an imperfect $c \neq 0$ and $a \neq 1$; that is, we would reach perfect discrimination. But practical men can and do circumvent the discrimination problem by raising or lowering *both*, that is, changing over-all survival rates, until one of either $a = 1$

or $c = 0$ is indeed approached. The consequences of approaching optimum by raising or lowering both is a *large* culture or *small* culture, respectively. What expressions (16) and (17) say is that it makes all the difference which one is encouraged in which kind of system. The single-screen case, for example, accords with intuition: it is best to clamp *down*. For, optimum lies as close as an imperfect world can approach $c = 0$. For example, movies have become better since the contraction of that culture in the 1950s, but popular music has become worse in the expansion of that culture since World War II.

The repetitive case is not intuitive, however, for its optimum size of surviving culture lies above even the very large cultures we achieve in the imperfect world of $a < 1$. And its best strategy is building *up* survival (that is, leniency) even though it is contrary, so to speak, to the Protestant aesthetic.

Yet the fact that severe survival standards are misguided in a repetitive system can be seen by writing the original expression for its final steady-state culture, S, in the following way:

$$S = A\left(\frac{1}{1-a}\right) + B\left(\frac{1}{1-b}\right) + C\left(\frac{1}{1-c}\right) \qquad (18)$$

The technical reader will find by turning back to expression (15), that the terms above in parentheses are equivalent to the earlier "multiples" of A, B, and C, respectively, that will be found in the final culture. Now, if we let over-all survival increase, $\Delta a = \Delta b = \Delta c = +$, the left denominators go toward $1 - 1 = 0$, and thus the terms become subject to volatile change on the left but only sluggish change on the right. The multiples of good material in the final culture are increased much more than those of the bad material when we increase over-all survival. And since the effect on S, the *size* of the culture, is the sum of these differential increases, better quality and larger size are as positively correlated in repetitive culture as are more wealth and larger savings.

As illustration, recall the earlier Table 3 where television parameters were used to calculate what three versions of that system would look like, first if it had single screening, next as television is now, and then as it could be with only one change, $a = .96$ (or the very best material averages about a generation's use). Let us now look at the raw *number* of programs involved in those calculations, assuming an annual input of 50 new programs a year, typical in recent years. Table 6 shows these data (where, as throughout, $A = .08$, $B = .20$, while strictly we only know that in recent years that together $A + B = .28$).

Table 6

Size of Television in Raw Programs under Assumptions of Table 3

Television as:	A Programs	B Programs	C Programs	=	S Total
Single-screening system:	8	18	44	=	70
Repetitive, as now ($a = .8$):	21	53	47	=	121
Repetitive, as now except $a = .96$:	100	53	47	=	200

The reader's attention is first invited to the parallelism between the left column for A programs and the right column for total size of culture, S. Down the table, as one applies the repetitive logic with increasing efficiency and thus with improving quality, there *must* be growth. But now note the total number of nighttime programs required to reach a minimum of one-half of television's offerings class A. It is a total of 200 at least. This is not only more than the 120 to 140 regular nighttime programs we find that television now tries out at one time or another during a broadcast season, including replacements for the replacements; but, if programs were good enough to command an hour's attention regularly all season, 200 programs is almost three times the available 70-odd hours of prime evening time a week on all three networks together. The latter is an arbitrary ceiling, then, clamped down on precisely what makes for quality, namely, accumulation.

An obvious suggestion is for television to do what virtually every other repetitive culture does, indeed, has to do, namely, decrease the *regularity* of performance of any one item in the repertory as that repertory accumulates in size. By our calculations, for example, an hour's performance every three weeks—or less than a dozen performances a broadcast season—would be consistent with the calculated potentialities above (i.e., a repertory of more than 200 regular programs of which more than 100 would be class *A*, that is to say, half the schedule consisting of the best one-tenth to one-twelfth of the entire generation's offerings and most of the rest satisfactory *B* material). This less frequent performance would also help the chief causes of loss of good material, in turn, overexposing the audience and overtaxing the creative talent.

Whatever the practical solution may be, however, it is not what practical men are doing today. For, that is as if we restricted our accumulated literature to what three people could read to us in seven evenings, or limited our store of classical music to what three orchestras could perform *every* week. This repertory would be not just a pitifully small culture, but a paradoxically poor one: a lot of *B* material invented last year and *C* rushed in last week, in the absence of the generation's best *A* offerings that could have survived as a collective repertory but were overworked to death in sequence individually. For, the consequence of a culture too small to accumulate material, "in parallel use," is to wear each item out in sequence.[7]

8. THE INTERACTION RULE

By "interaction" in culture we mean vicious or beneficent circles. For example, letting better material survive longer could

---

7. The point about "parallel" versus "sequential" use is much like an Army of 10 divisions that has the choice of fighting with many divisions at once or with one division at a time. The latter would be destroyed, and so on until none were left; but if all were used in parallel, the rate of attrition on each would be small enough to be balanced by recuperative powers.

provide the reward for attracting still better material; this still better material would, in turn, warrant lasting longer. There is an interaction like this between the parameters in the present model, expressed by the following rule.

If we consider jointly the best "input policy" affecting A and C and the best "discrimination policy" affecting a and c, the two best policies are at cross purposes in a single system, but mutually reinforcing in a repetitive system.

Specifically, what can be proved is that:

In a single system, the best discrimination policy, to decrease c, is motivation for and increases the effects from, the *least* effective input policy: to censor C.

In a repetitive system, the best discrimination policy, to increase a, is motivation for and increases the effects from, the *most* effective input policy: to foster A.

While it is unnecessary formally, it will add the cultural validity of the argument to appreciate a truth (and therefore to assume) that "motivation" attracting A input is in proportion a, its chance of success and longevity. And motivation repelling C input is in proportion $1 - c$, its chance of failure and shortlivedness. Thus, in the real world the ratio $A:B:C$ cannot remain unaffected by the ratio $a:b:c$.

Now, we already know what the best "discrimination policy" is, namely, in a repetitive system to increase a and in a single system to decrease c. The former would be motivation for, and thus mutually reinforce, an input policy of trying to motivate A, the latter an input policy trying to censor C. It remains to see whether these are, respectively, the best input policies.

This question first depends on the *rate* of improvement in the final amount of A material, the change δS_A, with a change now in the A proportion on input, δA, and analogously for C. These rates are

	Change in A	*Change in C*	
Single system:	$\dfrac{\delta S_A}{\delta A} = a$	$\dfrac{\delta S_C}{\delta C} = c$	(19)
Repetitive:	$\dfrac{\delta S_A}{\delta A} = \dfrac{1}{1-a}$	$\dfrac{\delta S_C}{\delta C} = \dfrac{1}{1-c}$	(20)

The result is clearcut: it *always* yields a faster rate of improvement in the final culture to foster A more than to censor C. This is true in the single case, first of all, because $a \gg c$. In other words, every A program added to input has a high chance of showing up in the final culture and thus making a difference, while a C program deleted from input makes little difference, because it had little chance of surviving in the final culture anyway. This same truth is intensified with a vengeance in the repetitive case, where the respective rates of improvement obtained, $1/(1-a) \gg 1/(1-c)$, are in ratio about 5.0 to 1.3 in television.

But if one refers back to expression (15) again, this rate $1/(1-a)$ is also equivalent to the "multiples of A" that one finds in the final culture. And that rate, in turn, is equivalent to the "longevity + 1" of the material. So we find that the rate of return from increasing A at input is the same as the longevity of A material in the system. This we found could be increased from 5 to 25 by reducing the annual loss of television's very best material from 20 per cent to about 4 per cent (or one program in every 25 best ones lost each year). In that event, we now find that improving input would really pay off: for every unit of A added to annual input, *25* units more of A would be added to the final culture!

Or, conversely, an unhappy ratings system that loses good material can vitiate the effect of good creation by as much as 20 multiples of that creation. We see, then, that the return from the best input policy, to increase A, interacts in a hypersensitive manner with a. But improving a, cutting down wheat errors, is in its own right the best discrimination policy in a repetitive system. Moreover, the earlier rate of return from increasing a can be written $A[1/(1 - a)^2]$, which means that the improvement from the best discrimination policy is *multiplied* by any increments, in turn, resulting from the best input (A) policy. The best policies, then, interact: the effect of increases in each intensifies the other's effect.

In fact, if we improve both simultaneously, tabulations show the effect on the final culture, namely, on S_A, reaches a volatile point, namely, when $A > 1 - a$. After that it "takes off" in the explosive manner of modern science and Western literature. In this kind of cultural explosion, however, it is not mainly improvements in A but in a—not good creation but good retention—that has the volatile effects, as can be seen from the *maximum* improvements one can expect if A goes all the way to 1, the best (utopia) one could hope for at the creative level. These maximum improvements at the input level (including also $C \to 0$) have the following effects:

	Change in A	*Change in C*
Repetitive:	$\displaystyle \operatorname*{Max}_{A\to 1} \Delta S_A = \frac{1 - A}{1 - a}$	$\displaystyle \operatorname*{Max}_{C\to 0} \Delta S_C = -\frac{C}{1 - c}$

The expression on the left would always be larger, confirming again that creating A, not criticizing C, is what pays off in the long run. Yet even in this extreme case of assuming all-A input, the return on the left expression would be moderate until and unless $1 - a$ errors were reduced toward zero. But when we do that, the direct return from that alone (without any improvement in input) is $+\infty$, as discussed earlier. All that we do by increasing A is to speed up the process. These expressions are for the final culture, and "infinity is a long wait" if there is not much A material coming in annually, for example, as in American sculpture. If we are patient, however—as illustrated by English poetry with its tiny input in the past but huge culture now—it is not the rate of creation but the rate of retention that has the finally decisive consequences in repetitive culture.

Compared with these prospects, the poor single systems—and thus most mass cultures as they are run today—are left so far behind that, in the writer's opinion, it is scarcely worth improving their input so long as these systems retain their present logic, the transient "hit" system in which today's improvement is gone tomorrow. The particular defect that turns up now is that their best input policy, also to increase A in a single system as well, does not increase the effects of the best discrimination policy, to reduce c. If we consider motivation, it is still worse. The success of the former policy of stimulating A input depends on a, both in formal consequences and in the sense of motivating reward for A input. But at the same time to clamp down on c, the best discrimination policy, means in an imperfect world to lower overall survival and thus to lower a. Clamping down, good policy alone, is at cross purposes with the best input policy.

An example is Broadway, which in the writer's judgment shows the best single-screening tactics today—the combination of fostering A input and clamping down on c survival. But having the best combination, it illustrates the inherent contradictions therein. For survival on Broadway has become so difficult and the resulting culture so small that we hear complaints today that A input has been discouraged to a small trickle in comparison to what playwriting for performance should in a nation of this size and affluence. One cannot have the small, exclusive culture needed for best discrimination and yet at the same time attract the creative effort that a short-run system needs more than a repetitive system, if it is going to replace its short-lived quality continuously with more quality.

Be that as it may, in the last half-century Broadway has moved toward what is not a bad *maximum* improvement possibility for input to a single-screening culture. Namely, the maximum returns from encouraging A or discouraging C are

$$\text{Single:} \quad \underset{A \to 1}{\text{Max}} \, \Delta S_A = (1 - A)(1 + a) \qquad \underset{C \to 0}{\text{Max}} \, \Delta S_C = -C(1 + c)$$

Change in A   *Change in C*

The left-hand term would always be larger, confirming what the rates implied as well: it always pays more to foster A than censor C, in principle. In practice, however, $A = 1$ is utopian where $C = 0$ is not; for example, probably no real C makes it to Broadway production today. And the term on the right, the return from eliminating C as Broadway has largely done in the last half-century, is sizable. So, Broadway probably took the road toward best *practical* improvement over the vaudeville and melo-

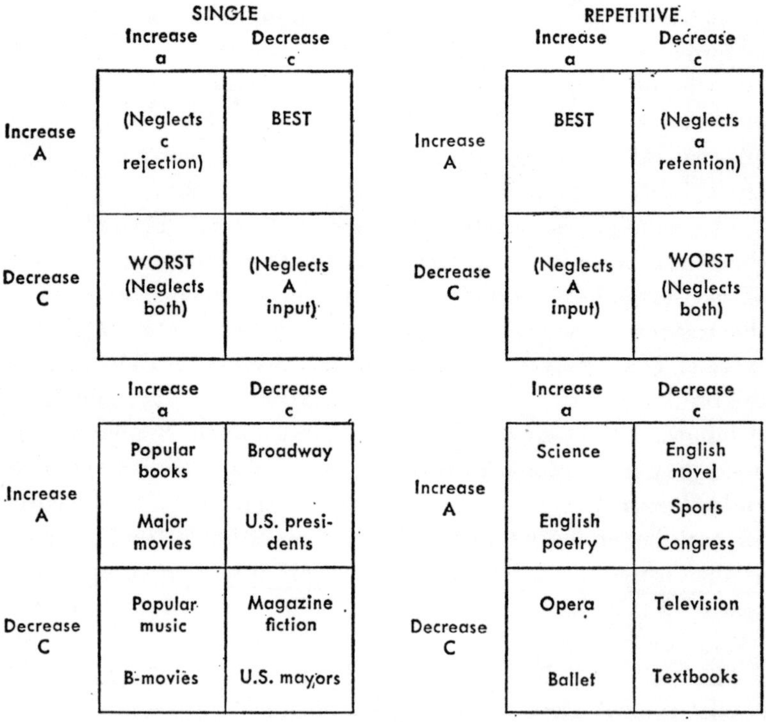

	SINGLE		REPETITIVE	
	Increase a	Decrease c	Increase a	Decrease c
Increase A	(Neglects c rejection)	BEST	BEST	(Neglects a retention)
Decrease C	WORST (Neglects both)	(Neglects A input)	(Neglects A input)	WORST (Neglects both)

	Increase a	Decrease c	Increase a	Decrease c
Increase A	Popular books Major movies	Broadway U.S. presidents	Science English poetry	English novel Sports Congress
Decrease C	Popular music B-movies	Magazine fiction U.S. mayors	Opera Ballet	Television Textbooks

Figure 3

Best and worst policy combinations (upper charts), with examples (lower charts.)

drama of the turn of the century, namely, foreclosing c rewards and thus ridding a single system of its nemesis, C. If this has bordered on ridding itself of everything, that is a dilemma inherent in the single system.

Figure 3 summarizes these arguments about interacting strategies and then illustrates the writer's guesses as to how data from various cultures might look if analyzed by this scheme. Only television data have been analyzed, however, and thus only its case is not purely opinion.

9. SUMMARY

The five principles that the model reveals as not only aesthetic but logical truths are that:

1. The repetitive logic is better.
2. Single screening is vulnerable to chaff errors, repetitive to wheat errors.
3. In a single system, low discrimination between B and C pays best, in a repetitive system high discrimination between A and B.
4. Size and quality are negatively correlated in a single system, positively correlated in a repetitive system.
5. The best input policy is at cross purposes with the best discrimination policy in a single system, but they are mutually reinforcing in the repetitive case.

As for the illustrative data from television, they lead to a diagnosis that, but for agonizingly missed opportunities, we could have a far better television culture than any of us suspect. Corresponding to the numbers above, television has (1) the right logic but (2) the damaging kind of error, because of (3) the wrong kind of discrimination and (4) from performing too small a repertory too often, so that (5) television has to do well what matters least, rejecting C, because it is not doing well what matters most, retaining A.

These things can be corrected, but the prognosis for other mass culture is gloomier, because the defect is in the very nature of what it is trying to do: create a new culture in each period that is better than the same people can create over many periods.

Technical Note

This note is in two parts: (1) first data are given on the survival of television programs in the past decade; and (2) then a solution for the model is discussed for those who wish to make other applications.

1. TELEVISION DATA

To repeat a previous note, I am indebted to Florence McClure for processing Nielsen data (see note 3). Table 7 gives the basic results.

The column headings are the number of seasons, 1, 2, 3, . . . , in which programs appeared *after* their baptismal season (which is period 0). This is also the number of eliminations survived. On the left is the identification of the baptismal year or time 0 in

Table 7

Proportion of Each Year's Input Surviving to 1, 2, 3, . . . , n Subsequent Seasons[a]

Input year, i.e., = time 0, and number of new programs, i.e. = 1.0	Proportion that appeared in — subsequent seasons, i.e., survived — eliminations										
	1	2	3	4	5	6	7	8	9	10	11
49–50 (129)	.45	.36	.24	.20	.15	.11	.09	.06	.02	.02	.02
50–51 (75)	.48	.31	.27	.23	.16	.11	.08	.07	.05	.04	
51–52 (61)	.49	.31	.21	.15	.13	.11	.11	.05	.05		
52–53 (42)	.50	.45	.29	.21	.17	.12	.12	.10			
53–54 (50)	.40	.26	.12	.10	.10	.08	.08				
54–55 (53)	.47	.34	.28	.23	.13	.06					
55–56 (42)	.50	.31	.19	.12	.12						
56–57 (46)	.37	.17	.13	.09							
57–58 (61)	.43	.25	.15								
58–59 (53)	.40	.25									
59–60 (56)	.25										

a. See text for explanation of table entries. A program occasionally skips a season, in which case we assume it survived continuously but was on the air one year less in total than the calendar interval. Programs skipping more than two years were considered new ventures the second time.

question and the raw number of programs originating that year, which is 1.0. Then the table entry is the proportion of those programs appearing in 1, 2, 3 . . . , n subsequent years.

These data cover only (a) network, (b) nighttime, 7:30–11:00 P.M. EST, programs that (c) appeared in Nielsen reports for the first two weeks of November *or* the first two weeks of February, but (d) do not include specials and other obviously irregular features, nor news as an obviously fixed feature. The programs on the air in 1949–50 are treated as "input" then (but 1949–50 data were not used in the text analysis).

2. SOLUTIONS FOR MODEL

To repeat an earlier note, I am indebted to Anthony Oberschall for the initial solution below. The model in the text with three classes of programs would lead to a cubic solution that, as we know from experience here and comparable problems in Lazarsfeld's latent-structure analysis, would tend to be unstable. So, instead we first solve a two-class model for C versus $1 - C$ using primarily data from the first two periods when C matters. Then we divide the residual class, $1 - C$, into A and B by solving iteratively for them.

The notation will be as in the text except that $1 - C = A + B$ and we let p stand for the average of a and b as the provisional probability that $A + B$ material together will survive any period. Then the *two*-class model is

$$s_0 = C + (1 - C) = 1.0 \tag{19}$$
$$s_1 = cC + p(1 - C) \tag{20}$$
$$s_2 = c^2C + p^2(1 - C) \tag{21}$$

and

$$S = \frac{1 - C}{1 - p} + \frac{C}{1 - c} \qquad (n \text{ large}) \tag{22}$$

where we will later replace (22) with an expression that does not require the steady state to be reached yet. For now, rewrite (22) as

$$S = \frac{(1 - c)(1 - C) + (1 - p)C}{(1 - p)(1 - c)}$$

which expands to

$$S(1 - p - c + cp) = (1 - c) + C(c - p)$$
$$S(1 - p) - Sc(1 - p) - (1 - c) = C(c - p)$$
$$S(1 - p)(1 - c) - (1 - c) = C(c - p)$$
$$(1 - c)[S(1 - p) - 1] = C(c - p)$$

But the earlier expression (20) can be rewritten to have the same term on the right:

$$s_1 - p = C(c - p) \tag{20a}$$

So that:

$$s_1 - p = (1 - c)[S(1 - p) - 1] \tag{23}$$

Returning to this equation shortly, we now rewrite the earlier expression (21) as

$$s_2 - p^2 = C(c^2 - p^2) \tag{21a}$$

And noting the similarity to (20a) just above, we can write (20a) and (21a) as

$$\frac{s_2 - p^2}{c^2 - p^2} = C = \frac{s_1 - p}{c - p}$$

$$\frac{s_2 - p^2}{c + p} = s_1 - p$$

$$s_2 - p^2 = cs_1 - cp + ps_1 - p^2$$

$$\frac{s_2 - cs_1}{s_1 - c} = p \tag{24}$$

Now substitute this value for p in expression (23) earlier:

$$s_1 - \frac{s_2 - cs_1}{s_1 - c} = (1 - c)\left[S\left(1 - \frac{s_2 - cs_1}{s_1 - c}\right) - 1 \right]$$

And, omitting routine details of the expansion of this equation, we finally have a quadratic equation for c in terms of otherwise observable quantities:

$$c^2(S - s_1 S - 1) + c(s_1 + s_2 S - S + 1) + (s_2 + s_1 S - s_2 S - s_1 - s_1^2) = 0 \tag{25}$$

There are potential difficulties with S as an "observable," however, since a system may not yet be in a steady state nor have an arbitrary ceiling as in television. So, recalling from the text that the expected longevity (in periods) of material with probability p of surviving one period is $p/(1 - p)$, we may define a weighted average of longevity as

$$\bar{k} = \frac{a}{1 - a} A + \frac{b}{1 - b} B + \frac{c}{1 - c} C \tag{26}$$

where $\bar{k}$ would then be the *observed* average longevity, the average number of successful survivals (that is, not counting period

0) before failure, of all the material together. Its implicit connection to S can be seen if we subtract it from the expression for S in a repetitive system:

$$
\begin{aligned}
S - \bar{k} &= \frac{A}{1-a} + \frac{B}{1-b} + \frac{C}{1-c} - \left(\frac{a}{1-a} A + \frac{b}{1-b} B \right. \\
&\qquad\qquad\qquad\qquad\qquad\qquad\qquad \left. + \frac{c}{1-c} C \right) \\
&= \frac{A}{1-a} (1-a) + \frac{B}{1-b} (1-b) + \frac{C}{1-c} (1-c) \\
&= A + B + C \\
&= 1
\end{aligned}
$$

and therefore

$$
S = \bar{k} + 1 \tag{27}
$$

This equation can be substituted for S in expression (25), since $\bar{k}$ or average trials survived would in most cases be more easily observed than the final steady-state size. Such a substitution gives (25) the following coefficients in its quadratic solution:

$$
c = \frac{-y \pm \sqrt{y^2 - 4xz}}{2x} \tag{28}
$$

where $x = \bar{k}(1 - s_1) - s_1$
$\qquad y = \bar{k}(s_2 - 1) + s_1 + s_2$
$\qquad z = \bar{k}(s_1 - s_2) - s_1^2$

Often one wishes to work, however, with material of such recent input that the $\bar{k}$ longevity of that particular material is not yet estimatable. In that event we can often, as in the case of television, suppose S to be fixed for the short period we are concerned with and thus that the new material is really "replacement" for dying material, as it is in television. If so, recalling that the annual input is 1.0 and the size of the culture S, then the fraction of the culture replaced, r, each year will be

$$
r = \frac{1}{S} = \frac{1}{\bar{k} + 1}
$$

so that

$$\bar{k} = \frac{1}{r} - 1 \tag{29}$$

This is how we estimated $\bar{k}$ for year-by-year input in television. Namely, in that system most of the elimination occurs in the first year after input, so if we wish to have a year-by-year estimate of $\bar{k}$ up to very recent years, the replacement needs the year following the input, r_{t+1}, sensitively reflect the durability of that input and thus yield a particular r to use in (29). This is the procedure we followed throughout, but some other average r could be used.

Now, since (28) and (29) give the estimate of c for a given input year, then p follows from (24). And, given c and p, we can rewrite the original (20) for C:

$$C = \frac{s_1 - p}{c - p} \tag{20b}$$

and the two-class model is thus determined. The solution uses primarily information from the first two eliminations when C and c matter, so we accept these estimates of them as sufficient.

Next the idea is that, with c and C known, we can use them to calculate the amount of C material at input and surviving at all times thereafter. By subtracting them *out* of observed data, what we have left is the behavior of A and B material alone. These data with C eliminated can then be solved for A and B in a two-class model, exactly as if they were the only material in a two-class system. To prepare the data for this two-class solution for A and B, define a new "input" unit, $s_0' = 1'$ as follows:

$$s_0' = 1' = (1 - C)N = |A + B|$$

where N is the raw number of original offerings and the notation on the right means this estimates the absolute number of A and B offerings at input. This was $1 - C$, but we now equate it with $1'$. Then the survival of these A and B programs alone through 1, 2, . . . , n subsequent eliminations, namely, s_1', s_2',

. . . , s_n', can be defined as

$$s_1' = \frac{(s_1 - cC)N}{(1 - C)N} = \frac{s_1 - cC}{1 - C}$$

$$s_2' = \frac{s_2 - c^2C}{1 - C}$$

$$s_n' = \frac{s_n - c^nC}{1 - C}$$

or the observed survivors less the calculated C survivors, as a proportion of $1 - C = A + B$ input. And now we need $\bar{k}'$ as the observed or calculated average survival of A and B material alone. One expression for it is

$$\bar{k}' = \frac{\bar{k} - \dfrac{c}{1 - c}C}{1 - C}$$

which is obtained by dividing (26) by $1 - C = A + B$ and then noting:

$$\frac{\dfrac{a}{1 - a}A + \dfrac{b}{1 - b}B}{A + B} = \bar{k}'$$

or the (weighted) average longevity for A and B material alone. One could also define

$$\bar{k}' = \frac{1}{r'} - 1$$

where r' is now the replacement needs for A and B material, or

$$r' = \frac{1 - C}{S - \dfrac{C}{1 - c}}$$

the numerator being the $A + B$ input and the denominator being the size of the culture, less C material.

This elimination of C from the observed data is much easier in those data than the formulas suggest. Then one simply defines a new two-class model:

$$s_1' = aA' + bB'$$
$$s_2' = a^2A' + b^2B'$$
$$S' = \frac{A'}{1-a} + \frac{B'}{1-b}$$
$$\bar{k}' = \frac{a}{1-a} A' + \frac{b}{1-b} B'$$

and the solution proceeds exactly as before. Now C in the original solution is B', $1 - C$ now becoming A', c now b, and p now a. The notation A' and B' is to remind the calculator, however, that these add to 1 in the two-class model, and it will be necessary to convert by the relations $A'(1 - C) = A$ and $B'(1 - C) = B$ to combine with the original solution for C to add to 1 in a final three-class model.

The failure of the three-class model in the case of television took the form that A disappeared (was negative, zero, or at best in some years a few per cent), with the remaining $B \approx 1 - C$ surviving at a rate not substantially different from the provisional p in the original two-class solution. As explained in the text, this conclusion is verified by inspection of the ratios, s_i/s_{i-1}.

The estimate of C and c by this method is good because s_1, s_2, and r all characterize the *early* survival picture. For the same reason, however, the estimates for b and a are not efficient by this method, because the method does not use the later information through s_n, where a and b matter most. In concrete cases, however, one can usually find some kind of averaging procedure. A tedious one is to define "input" as various $s_i = s_0$ and repeat the solutions with $s_1 = s_{i+1}$, $s_2 = s_{i+2}$, and so on, to find what values of a and b best fit points along the tail of the distribution. Work is needed, however, on efficient estimates of a and b.[8]

8. Related work is in Leo Goodman and Albert Madansky, "Parameter-free and Non-parametric Tolerance Limits: The Exponential Case," *Technometrics*, Vol., 4 No. 1, Feb., 1962.

A Theory of Informal Social Influence

2

*with Jack Ferguson
and Robert B. Smith*

1. INTRODUCTION

The purpose of this paper[1] is to describe a social influence process that is not vulnerable to the objections raised by psychologists and political scientists to what they call excessive "sociologizing" in the explanation of choices.[2]

1. The initial work on this paper drew on funds from a grant to the first author by the Behavioral Sciences Division of the Ford Foundation. It was revised and all runs replicated with funds from a grant by the Social Science Division of the National Science Foundation, NSG G# 13045. Machine time on an IBM 650 was freely supplied by Watson Scientific Computing Laboratory at Columbia University.
2. For example, V. O. Key, Jr., and Frank Munger, "Social Determinism and Electoral Decision: The Case of Indiana," in *American Voting Behavior*,

The choices here happen to be votes—although the process to be described is not limited to this application. What is meant by "social influence" is the observation that people in close contact for long periods, such as husbands and wives or parents and children, are found to have remarkably nonindependent preferences. At any given time, their choices are highly correlated. What is meant by objectionable "sociologizing" of this phenomenon, however, are interpretations of how these correlations come about over time. It is too easy to make the choice *itself* a function of deliberate social manipulation by others or conscious adaptation to others.

No one really advocates this kind of "social determinism," however. Nearly everyone admits the necessity, and most of us the primacy, of two other determinants of the immediate choice: namely, (1) external political stimuli such as current events and (2) internal psychological dispositions such as political party loyalties learned in the past. But if we admit the primacy of these brute facts, then how can responses to them nevertheless be so correlated with the subtle cues from others in the contiguous social environment?

This paper describes a social influence process that has the desired subtlety. It leaves the determination of the choice at all times to external (that is, political) stimuli and individual (that is, psychological) dispositions. Working through these, however, such a process is capable of generating any of the social correlations found in choice data.

2. A THREE-PROCESS MODEL OF VOTING

The influence process to be described is one of three processes that make up a model for the study of voting behavior. It is no accident that the other two processes concern the primary determinants of voting referred to above: the response to external

Eugene Burdick and Arthur J. Brodbeck, eds. (New York: The Free Press Glencoe, 1959), pp. 281–307.

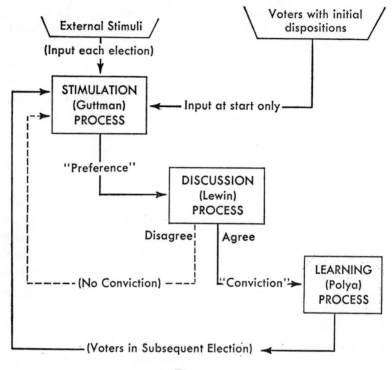

Figure 1

Flow chart of the model.

stimuli and the learning of internal dispositions. The complete model has been described in detail elsewhere.[3] It was designed and is being used for large problems of national scope and historical time spans.[4] Therefore, the processes by which a single individual forms a single vote in one election are necessarily too simple to be interesting as psychological theories. Here they will

3. William N. McPhee and Robert B. Smith, "A Model for Analyzing Voting Systems," in *Public Opinion and Congressional Elections*, William N. McPhee and William A. Glaser, eds. (New York: The Free Press of Glencoe, 1962).

4. For example, William N. McPhee and Jack Ferguson, "Political Immunization," in McPhee and Glaser, *op. cit.*

be briefly explained—and with a certain amount of literary license—by the flow diagram of Figure 1.

This model is operated in a computer. We shall assume that a large sample of "voters," representing a community in some political period, has already been put into the machine storage or memory of the computer. Each voter is represented by a limited series of characteristics, many of which will be modified by events during each election period. Let us assume that we are about to start an "election," as one of a sequence of them.

The model first takes from the input hopper an injection of "political stimuli" for the period since the last election. These are distributions of stimuli graded as to their attractiveness or cogency from strong to weak. The distributions differ for different groups in the sample electorate, as determined by needs of the problem not relevant here.

The *stimulation* process is shown in the upper left-hand block of Figure 1. It assigns a particular stimulus to each individual voter by a Monte Carlo method. This method preserves the distributions of strong and weak stimuli from the party to the voter *group* affected. But within that restriction, for any individual voter the assignment is at random. This has an important consequence for present purposes. If for any reason this voter repeats the stimulation process, he may *not* get the same impression (level of stimulus). This difference is analogous to a voter's getting a different impression of a party on reconsideration in October from his first casual impression in May. With the exception of this stochastic flavor—the justification for which can be found in the work of Wiggins among others[5]—the stimulation process follows a rule most of us take for granted as a truism.

A. The stronger the individual's internal disposition towards a party, the *weaker* the external stimulus required to elicit a "yes" choice for that party.

5. Lee M. Wiggins, "Mathematical Models for the Interpretation of Attitude and Behavior Change: The Analysis of Multi-Wave Panels, 1955, unpublished Ph.D. dissertation, Columbia University.

B. Conversely, the weaker the internal disposition of an individual towards a party, the *stronger* the external stimulus required to elicit a "yes" choice for that party.[6]

Recognition that this is how people respond to questionnaire stimuli, if those are all on the same topic and differ only in cogency or attractiveness, has been made explicit by, among others, Louis Guttman's scaling procedures.[7] Therefore, for a label, call the stimulation process a "Guttman process." Its output is an initial preference for one of the two choices (parties), although under certain circumstances voters develop no preference for either party and become incipient nonvoters. This initial preference may be likened to a first impression of a situation that may be changed by later reflection.

Next, note the *discussion* process shown at the center of Figure 1. The initial preferences above are its input, and this process produces as its output surviving preferences, that is to say, preferences that survive discussion and the reflection it may prompt. A surviving preference can be interpreted as the final "conviction" about how to vote at election time; but here we will be less concerned with the vote than with how anything that helped reach that conviction also affects *learning* (modification of dispositions) and thus the individual's future behavior. Hence, returning later to discuss social influence—our main topic—let us first see how the learning process operates.

As suggested by its location at the lower right of Figure 1, the learning process takes as input the convictions surviving the discussion process and its output is some modification of the dis-

6. See "A Campaign Simulator" in this volume, and Part III of "Attitude Consistency," in McPhee and Glaser, *op. cit.*, for a more formal treatment of the stimulation process.

7. Louis Guttman, "The Basis for Scalogram Analysis," in *Measurement and Prediction*, Vol. IV of the series "Studies in Social Psychology in World War II," Samuel A. Stouffer, ed., Vol. IV (Princeton, N.J.: Princeton University Press, 1950). In psychology, like ideas date back to Thurstone.

position that will affect choices in the subsequent elections. To give the name "learning" to this is perhaps a euphemism, although the mathematical models of learning in psychology are equally simple.[8] In its most elementary form, the gist of the present idea is identical to certain "urn models" worked out in mathematics to fit the growth of disease and similar self-developing or progressively intensifying phenomena. The rule is, in oversimplification adequate for present purposes, that

A. The more often one chooses a party now, the more likely he is to prefer the *same* party in the future.

B. Which is implemented by making the probability of preferring a party the same as the *frequency* of (weighted) preferences for it, each new one thus adding to the probability.

While this learning process was designed without knowledge of the above urn models of progressive phenomena, one by G. Polya most resembles the present case, which we therefore call a "Polya process."

The disposition that is modified is a general probability of choosing each of the alternatives. A high probability of choosing one political party *and* a low one of choosing the other, for example, would correspond to what we call "party loyalty." In any event, these modified dispositions then form the input, with new stimuli, for the stimulation process in the next cycle, for example, the next election.

3. THE INFLUENCE PROCESS

Let us now retrace steps to cover more detail the process in the middle of Figure 1, whose inputs, to repeat, are initial im-

8. The present learning process has a resemblance to the models of William K. Estes, that is, the cumulative learning of sampled elements from a "stimulus" that is actually a distribution of such elements. Estes models can be shown, in turn, to be formally equivalent to that of Bush and Mosteller. For the Polya process, see Note 10, Introduction.

pressions gained from the stimulation process and whose outputs are surviving convictions affecting learning.

The latter convictions may be reached by either of two routes. One we shall call "social-reality testing." This idea is associated with the name Kurt Lewin, and so we call (this aspect of) the discussion routine a "Lewin process."

Lewin's idea was simple. Suppose that we want to test the truth of a belief. One can often do this by objective means. If he wants to find out whether glass will break if hit with sufficient force by an object, then he can actually try to break some. This will be a test against the criterion of "objective reality." But, suppose one gets the idea that, say, Governor Rockefeller would make a good President. There is no easy way to determine the truth of this proposition; and few of us, as voters, have the means to test it.

Consciously or not, many of us adopt an alternative kind of criterion: we *ask* somebody, preferably somebody from New York. What does he think about Governor Rockefeller? Or we notice how others react to the Presidential candidates and who people around us think is best. If others agree with our own impression, we retain it. And so this initial impression will tend to survive— our own judgment confirmed by others—and grow into a conviction. Lewin called this kind of cross-checking with others the testing of a belief against the criterion of "social reality." In ambiguous situations, where the cost of objective testing is prohibitive, everyone would agree that "social reality" is the only test criterion.

This cross-checking one's own impressions against the social reality of other's impressions is accomplished in the present model as follows. People in the sample (computer) population are tied together in sociometric nets representing intimate contact, for example, family members and close friends. If two such people have sufficient interest in politics (their joint interest adds to more than an indifference point), they "discuss" the topic, and their initial preferences now become visible to one another. Then the following happens:

If a voter's own initial impression *agrees* with that of his intimate friend or parent during the discussion process, then doubts are set at rest. The initial reaction is "confirmed" as an acceptable choice. The significance is that this will probably be the choice learned, that is, the one that modifies future dispositions towards a party. And this is as it should be in any learning process. For, from the standpoint of the person, this confirmed choice was the product of (1) his own reaction to objective stimuli and (2) the one socially rewarded as well.

The case of *disagreement* is handled in a way that provides a complement to Lewin's notion. One must always keep in mind that political stimuli are never wholly ambiguous. They have a rational reality that is often compelling despite contrary social advice (which we know is often wrong). When other persons disagree with our impressions of reality, we are just as likely to suspect the others' opinion is wrong as we are to suspect that we ourselves interpreted reality incorrectly. If both are suspect then, it means that social reality has become ambiguous. In that event, who or what is the arbitrator?

Obviously, it is objective reality again. Just as social reality is the arbitrator when objective reality is ambiguous, so objective reality is the arbitrator when social reality is ambiguous.

In the model, this last effect is accomplished by renewed exposure (after such social disagreement) to the external stimuli again. In the model's version now running, both disagreers are simply sent back through the stimulation process again. Each voter again forms impressions by sampling the distributions of external stimuli, as these interact with his internal political dispositions exactly as before. A new preference comes out of this second exposure. The rule for deciding between the former and the new preference is:

A. If the new preference is the same as his former one, then the voter has "confirmed himself" and will retain his *old* preference despite contrary advice.

B. If his preference is different and now accords with the impression of his social intimate, he will adopt his new preference (because his *own* recheck against reality confirms the advice he received).

It happens that the preference retained is logically identical, in either event, to the one resulting from the voter's own impression on the second trip through the stimulation process.

Complications arise in how to handle repetitive occurrences of this process in the same election and other problems. One can therefore expect that many variants of the process will emerge in future simulation programs, especially in application to different fields, of which we discuss one in a Technical Note. But in any such variant there is one central idea—that the voter makes up his *own* mind and social influences merely assist him to determine which of his samplings or impressions of reality is stable in the face of cross checks.

4. SOCIALIZATION EFFECT

Let us turn now to some results illustrating how this influence process behaves. Because the model is a long-term one, designed especially to deal with political generations, a primary function we demand of any social influence process is to reproduce the facts of political *socialization*. That is, it should be able to make loyal Democrats and partisan Republicans out of youths who at first have unpredictable tendencies. Figure 2 gives an illustration of how the combination of discussion and learning processes work together to accomplish this.

The data of Figure 2 were generated with the following experimental (hypothetical) input:

1. Half of the machine population represented very young people, for example, ten to fifteen years old. "Very young" has a technical meaning here equivalent to little past experience in politics (which is therefore easily modified by new experience).[9]

2. This starting experience was such that these youths would, if left to themselves, have about *equal* probabilities of voting for both parties, as well as some probabilities of not voting.[10]

3. Each such young voter was then tied, in a friendship or sociometric network, to the equivalent of a *parent* with much political experience. That parental experience was biased almost wholly to favor one party.[11]

This experimental setup means that when the youth develops initial preferences in ensuing elections during his teens and early twenties, he is discussing his choice with a strongly partisan parent who is, most of the time, unwavering in his convictions. With this approximation of reality in, say, Iowa Republican families and New York City Democratic families, what we want to know is whether the same discussion process by which adults influence each other will socialize children as well. This was determined by holding a sequence of elections corresponding to the decade or two during which youths are first taking some interest in politics, but are still not independent of their elders' coaching or example. Nine elections happened to be run, and in all elections

9. The learning process above and as described in detail in McPhee and Smith, *op. cit.*, computes the probability that serves as disposition to vote for a party as a frequency roughly like, omitting weights, this:

$$\Pr\{\text{Dem.}\} = \frac{\text{No. of Democratic choices}}{\text{No. of all choice opportunities}}$$

The absolute magnitudes involved, that is, of the denominator, make the process unstable if they are small, stable if they are large. In the particular experiment, whereas the denominator was 28 units for adults (the "parents" of the text), it was 10 for youths.

10. The youths were given, in footnote 9, four units of Democratic choice, four Republicans, and two neither party.

11. The parents were 24 units for one party, one for the other, and three neither.

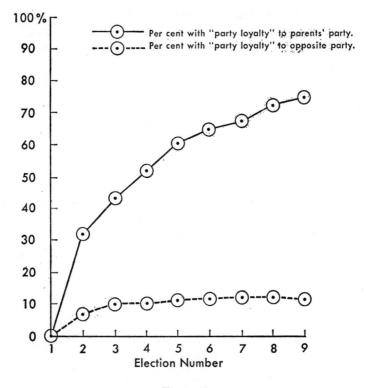

Figure 2

The growth of "party loyalty." (Party loyalty = high probability of voting for one party *and* low probability of voting for the other.)

here the distributions of stimuli for each party were equal and normal.[12]

What Figure 2 shows is the percentage of youths who develop the kind of one-sided dispositions called "party loyalty." This

12. "Normal" refers to a rectangular distribution where all strengths of stimuli are equally likely, in McPhee and Smith, *op. cit.* If the individual were alone, it would simply translate party dispositions (probabilities) into manifest preferences (corresponding frequencies). For example, of those with 0.7 probability of voting for a party, 70 per cent of the cases would actually do so.

means a high probability of voting for one party and a low probability of voting for the other. The upper trend line shows the percentage of youths who developed party loyalty for the *parents'* party and the lower trend line those who developed loyalty for the opposite party, all having started with equal tendencies in both directions and thus no such loyalty.[13]

If each election is considered to have taken place at the end of a two-year period, then it can be seen that the direction of the two trend-lines was well established after four or five elections, or a decade of political activity. If we had released the youths from their parental influence at the end of the first decade, they would have *continued* to vote for the same party during the second decade. For what is shown in Figure 2 is a measure of the growth of internalized dispositions. In this model, as in real life, after a time external guidance is no longer required, for its effect is now perpetuated by inner conviction.

5. ADULT DISPOSITIONS

So much for socialization. The power of the influence process seems so great in that function that one immediately fears it would be "too strong" for purposes of the less effective social influence among adults. This is not so. In the above socialization experiment we gave each youth equal dispositions towards both parties at the beginning of the period. And the distributions of stimuli for each party for all persons were also equal in all periods in order to show the effect of the discussion process when all other things were equal—all other things *except* the sustained influence exerted by partisan parents. But in adult political life all other things are not equal.

13. Population size for computer simulation shown in Figure 2—the number of *youths* involved—is approximately 400 for each election in the sequence of nine, in four independent replications of 100 each. Of course, a larger population would be necessary for precise quantitive study of such curves, not the purpose here.

Table 1

Distribution of Cases in a National Sample by Estimated Probabilities of Voting for Each Party

Probability of Voting Democrat[a]

		.0	.1	.2	.3	.4	.5	.6	.7	.8	.9
	.0	522	142	158	58	62	84	71	70	61	296
	.1	65	75	21	21	5	1	—	—	—	—
	.2	100	6	67	6	25	51	24	57	12	—
Probability of Voting Republican	.3	54	13	3	17	—	29	—	17	—	—
	.4	50	—	6	—	3	1	8	—	—	—
	.5	95	—	25	12	—	33	—	—	—	—
	.6	64	—	5	—	—	—	—	—	—	—
	.7	75	—	33	16	—	—	—	—	—	—
	.8	73	—	14	—	—	—	—	—	—	—
	.9	229	—	—	—	—	—	—	—	—	—

a. The table entry is the number of Roper interviews out of a sample of 2,936 cases, September, 1956.

A main reason has just been shown. Precisely the effect of social influences themselves, via socialization, is to make dispositions toward the two parties unequal. Thus, we later find in an adult population relatively few people who are still equally "influenceable" in any direction. This finding is illustrated by Table 1.

Table 1 was prepared by classifying every adult respondent in a Roper survey in 1956. The classification was by an estimated probability of the person voting Democrat (top of table) and his estimated probability of voting Republican (left-hand side of table). This classification was done by relatively crude means, to serve as input to the model;[14] but with these survey respond-

14. Thanks are due the Roper Opinion Research Center, Williams College, for this information, and for its processing to a research group at IBM, Inc., headed by Eugene Lindstrom. The index was constructed by first assigning to each person a "turnout" probability, or probability to vote, which was based on the relative *frequencies* with which he expressed interest, had previously voted and expressed intention to vote. Each person was then

ents as its "voters," the model behaves accurately for the 1956 election period.

The table shows the (raw) number of survey respondents for every combination. The main result for present purposes is that the bulk of the cases fall along the top and the left-hand margins. This means that most of the people have some probability of voting for one party but very little for the other party. Only those few individuals in the center cells around the main diagonal have approximately equal probabilities of voting for either party. We can see by the small numbers of the latter that in the adult world other things are *seldom* equal. Let us turn, therefore, to the effects of the discussion process where other things are un-equal—the real-life circumstance.

6. INFLUENCE AND DISPOSITION AT CROSS PURPOSES

A new experiment was designed using youths and adults of the same characteristics as before. The difference now is that the little experience in politics given the youths is biased. And it is biased towards the party *opposite* that of the parents. This experiment could be considered a simulation of the New Deal period, where, even before voting age, many youths were learning to like Roosevelt's party, despite Republican parents. Specifically, a probability of 0.2 was assigned for voting for the parents' party and 0.6 of voting for the opposite party. This design ensured that there would be disagreement between youths and parents ranging between 70 and 90 per cent in all variations of the experiment.

---

assigned a "directional" probability based upon party identification, previous vote for Senator or Governor, and previous Presidential vote. What is shown as the table entry here is the joint probability, multiplying probabilities of voting turnout and of directional or party choice. Equal weights for all items in the index is assumed here, but current work with latent-structure scaling that does not require that assumption does not seem to lead to significantly different results.

The variations mentioned were introduced to represent different political climates (stimulus situations). These aided or hindered the youths' tendencies to go against their parents' traditional party. Specifically:

A. One is a "control" variant. Here stimuli for the youths' party—party their dispositions favored (0.6 probability)—were *equal* to stimuli for the parents' party (for which youths had only 0.2 probability). This is identical, except for the youths' biased disposition, to the above experiment.

B. Another is a "strong" variant. Here the youths' own party —the party their dispositions favored—offered *stronger* stimuli throughout the period than did the opposite party, that is, the party of the parents, since parents and youths disagreed.[15]

C. Finally, in a "weak" variant, the youths' own party offered *weaker* stimuli throughout the period than did the opposite party for which they had weaker dispositions—again the party of the parents.

These three variations of the experiment were run for the same number of elections as before. Results are shown in tables and charts in much of the remainder of this paper.

A key result, in Table 2, is a measure of the effectiveness (when there is disagreement) of parents in *changing* the youths' preferences. Recall what happens after disagreement occurs in the voting model. The youth goes back through the stimulation process again. This is interpreted as reconsidering reality in the face of a social situation that is not supporting the original choice. The youth gets a new preference from repeating the stimulation process. It may be quite different from the first impression because the process is in part governed by chance events (sampling

15. "Strong" refers to a *distribution* of stimuli. If, for example, there were five grades of stimuli from the strongest to the weakest, then the probability of each occurring is, respectively, .30, .25, .20, .15, .10. (See McPhee and Smith, *op. cit.*) The "weak" distribution used is .10, .15, .20, .25, .30, as the frequencies of occurrence of strongest to weakest stimuli, respectively.

Table 2

The Outcome of Youths' Second Stimulation
after Initial Disagreement with Parents

AFTER DISAGREEMENT WITH PARENTS YOUTHS' DIRECTION
OF CHANGE WAS:

		Towards Parents	No Change	Farther Away from Parents	
	Strong	13%	78%	9%	100%
Youths' *own* party stimuli	Normal	25%	60%	15%	100%
	Weak	40%	43%	17%	100%

of grades of stimulus strengths). A count is kept by the computer of these changes. The direction of change after the disagreement is what is shown as the table entry of Table 2. For simplicity figures shown are averages for all elections in several independent replications on this problem.[16]

For example, when the youths' own party was given strong stimulation, only 13 per cent of the youths changed to the parents' party. Actually, 100 per cent could have changed, since the table considers only those who initially disagreed with parents. A full 78 per cent of the youths kept their original choice. The remaining 9 per cent are those who were originally not intending to vote, but who now decided to vote for the party opposite that of the parents. So, almost nine out of ten youths *resisted* the parents' advice when political stimuli favored the party towards which their own internal dispositions also leaned.

The center row of Table 2 shows the normal or control case and the bottom row the situation where the stimuli of the youths' own party were weak. The latter illustrates a condition for effectiveness of social influence in causing changes against the direction of the youths' internal disposition. The condition for effective influence is when *objective* reality (the stimulus distribution) is

16. *N* for each *row* of Table 2 is about 200, in four independent replications, for any one election, and we average nine elections.

contrary to internal disposition. Otherwise, other than when the youths' own party stimuli were weak, the parents' counsel was not effective against youths' dispositions that were now in the opposite direction.

Table 2 shows only about half of the potential influence, however. It does not show what happens when the youth happens to *agree*, initially, with the parent's party choice. Then, of course, the youth is encouraged to keep that preference. This positive encouragement in the case of agreement is discussed later as a "reinforcement" phenomenon.

The sizable joint effect of both of these types of influence is summarized in Table 3. The sample base is now all the youths (not only those who disagreed initially as in Table 2). The matter of concern is now the final choice regardless of how it was reached, that is, the vote.[17] It is averaged for the first decade in the upper table and for the second decade in the lower.

A set of additional runs is added, however, with which to compare the cases we have been considering. The latter, whose tendency was contrary to the parents, are the cases shown in the *right*-hand column. On the left are the new cases. They are identical in all respects except that they tend to *agree* with their parents. (Youth's probability of voting for parent's party is here 0.6, for the opposite party 0.2, the mirror opposite of the above.)

The table entry in all cases is the rate of voting for the youth's "own party," the one his internal dispositions favor, 0.6 to 0.2. On the left side, where parents agree, this is also the parent's party, and influence is in the same direction as the disposition. On the right side, the vote for the party favored by the disposition is being cast *despite* contrary influence. Comparing the rows, then, gives the difference due to influence compatible with dispositions versus influence against dispositions, under different stimulus conditions down the columns.

---

17. *N* is about 200 for each *cell* of Table 3, in independent replications as above.

Table 3

**Per Cent of Youths Voting for Their *Own* Party: The Party of
Their Initial Disposition**

		FIRST DECADE	
		When Parents' Party Is the *Same* as Youths' Party	When Parents' Party Is *Opposite* Youth's' Party
Youths' *own* party stimuli	Strong	97%	80%
	Normal	88%	59%
	Weak	71%	31%
		SECOND DECADE	
Youths' *own* party stimuli	Strong	98%	79%
	Normal	93%	57%
	Weak	75%	24%

To summarize the results: Social influence here makes only a minor difference in the extent to which youth votes for the party of its own inclinations, when that party is offering strong stimuli (top row).

When the stimuli are not so strong, however, the story is different. The middle row lists the situation where the stimuli for the youths' own party are normal and equal to the other party. This is the ambiguous case of no reliable guidance either way from external reality. The difference that an encouraging versus a discouraging parent makes, here, is quite sizable and increases still more in the second decade. In the third row, where the youths' party is offering weak stimuli in this period, a big vote for that party never materializes when the parents are in opposition (right side). The revolt, so to speak, "aborts" when objective or external reality fails to support it.

Here is something curious, however. When parents *do* support this objectively weak position, agreeing with the youth's own disposition (left side), the vote for it remains sizable despite the weak stimuli from external reality. It suggests the real-life counterpart when social influence "insulates" a compatible disposition from contrary reality, as, for example, a dense distribution of Republicans in Vermont tended to insulate youth there from political trends in the 1930s contrary to their dispositions.

7. CHANGE IN DISPOSITION VERSUS VOTE

Yet, in the actual world, does discussion alone "really" change people? We are all familiar with compliant behavior without change of feeling. To examine this, note that we have to this point been discussing single preferences, or discrete votes in one election. "Really" to change a person, however, might mean to change his basic dispositions toward the two parties. The latter are sluggish in this model. Many a borderline or chance vote can be changed, but to alter party dispositions requires (1) a sustained influence that is (2) working under ideal conditions. Figure 3 illustrates this feature of the model's behavior.

We again consider only the original sample, where all youths start with a disposition *contrary* to their parents' party. We also retain the three experimental variants, with the rebellious youth's party strong, normal, and weak in its stimulus offerings (for example, appeal of candidates). The table entry in Figure 3 is now different, however. It is not votes but the "party loyalty" concept. Specifically, it is the percentage of the youths with high probability of voting for "their own" party, the one we started them inclining towards, combined with a low probability of voting for their opposing parents' party. In effect, the table entry is the percentage of the incipient rebellions that are becoming *permanently* successful by a given time, the higher the proportion in Figure 3 the more youths have become (almost irreversibly) committed to the party they inclined toward but their parents did not.[18]

18. N is 200 for each point (election) on each time path, each independently replicated in smaller samples.

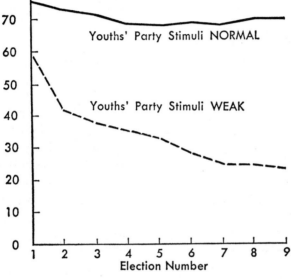

Figure 3

Per cent of youths with "party loyalty" to that party favored by their initial dispositions. (Party loyalty = high probability of voting for one party *and* low probability of voting for the other.) Parents' party is opposite in all examples.

In the model, at least, the outcome is clearcut: When the party of the youths' own disposition offers him strong stimuli, his loyalty to it is untouched by contrary social influence. In fact it grows. When the youths' own party's stimuli are normal—equal to those of the other party—the result is also a resistance to social influence (after an initial minor effect) on what "really" matters, the disposition. Earlier, we saw that substantial differences in *votes* in any given election were attributable to contrary social influence in this situation (see Table 3). But here the deeper party *dispositions*, once given a direction early in the socialization process, are not really reversed by the impressions and advice that, it is true, affect discrete votes. All this simulates a kind of "accommodation": overt behavior that conforms to the environment is more common than underlying disposition change.

The latter kind of fundamental reorientation, a reversal of a previous disposition, is rare in real life for the same reason as in the model. It occurs only in the extreme example, where not only a sustained social influence is consistently contrary over a substantial period, but the influence is also always supported by the objective reality of external events (lower time path in Figure 3). That is, it requires that, when the parent tells a youth that his rebellious party's offerings are actually weak, when the youth reconsiders these offerings, he finds that indeed they are weak. Thus, social direction of basic dispositions is only heeded, in this model, where it *should* be.

Such a situation so ideally favorable to the influence over many elections seldom happens, however. So the gist of the results as we approach adulthood, *after* socialization or other causes have started dispositions in one direction, is that thereafter social influence alone cannot reverse that direction. This realistic example completes the illustration that a process strong enough to produce the striking correlations in socialization data (for example, 70 per cent or more people voting for the same party as their parents did) is at the same time a *weak* enough process to accord with common-sense observations of adults. Namely, for all that they do and rationally should consult one another on specific choices, they resist one another's efforts to change deeper internal allegiances.

8. AN ILLUSTRATIVE IMPLICATION

The examples of this paper do not differ for those usually introduced in support of a verbal theory: they are already known from everyday experience or past research. That the model can reproduce them says something for their explanation and for its validity. The main hope for these methods, of *working* models and therefore working theory, is, however, that they will generate *new* implications not previously apparent from the static verbal statement of the same theory. At this early stage of experience little has been delivered on that promise, but we conclude with a small example.

The process above was designed with "reconsideration" as the central idea; then its similarity to Lewin's "social reality" was noted. But now note that the same formal logic can also be interpreted as "reinforcement theory," as in experiments on animal learning. There the environment (played by the experimenter) *selects* out of large number of randomlike behaviors of the animal that which is to be rewarded. The stimulation process in the present model generates the same kind of partially random behavior of subjects (youths' preferences). Then the influence process plays a role like that of the experimenter, selecting *which* of these partly random preferences it will choose to reinforce (pass on to the learning process).

So, here Lewinian and reinforcement theories turn out to be representable by the same logic (computer program). The difference is simply heuristic, namely, where one locates himself as observer. Lewin takes the introspectionist point of view of the subjects (animals, voters) who are discovering which behavioral choice is the valid one, that is, the best way to vote or get food. The behaviorist takes the point of view of the experimenter (environment, parent) waiting for the subjects to propose the choice he will select as the valid one that gets the reward.

The latter view of the model has an interesting implication in politics. An example is shown in Figure 4. The points along the time paths in Figure 4 plot the vote of youths for the party towards which originally they inclined in initial disposition, "their own party" as before (their probability of choosing it 0.6 versus 0.2 for the other). The top line on each side show the vote in cases where the parent's party is the *same* as the youths. The bottom line on each side plots the vote of youths for their party when the parent's party is opposite. Thus, the "gap" between the two lines is a measure of the difference that a consistently favorable versus a consistently unfavorable social environment makes in voting for the party of one's own initial inclinations.

The stimulus situation for the two parties now differs from previous experiments. One party is offering *constant* stimuli of the normal or control type of distribution, as before. But the other party is offering *oscillating* stimuli, first being favored and then later disfavored by "great historical events." For example, the second and sixth elections are "booms," like 1936 for the Democrats. The fourth and eighth elections are "disasters" of equal and opposite magnitude against the same party.[19]

The difference between the two diagrams of Figure 4 is that in the left-most one it is the youths' own party that offers an oscillating stimulus pattern. In the right-hand chart it is the opposite party that is oscillating. If we think of resistance to influence as depending on the "support" one gets from his *own* party's offerings, these are what vary in the left chart. On the other hand, if we think of the effectiveness of influence as depending on the "temptations" offered by the influencer's side, the other side, then the attractiveness of these temptations is what is variable in the right chart.

Magnitudes and timing are otherwise identical. So, what Figure 4 suggests is that, while response changes more in this case where "support" for one's own cause is varying, the effect of the *social* influence is greater when "temptations" toward the other cause are varying. This is seen by the large gap at the end of the experiments in the right-hand chart. Why is that?

First, consider the case when parents or other influences want

19. Booms are created by introducing "strong" stimulus distributions as in footnote 15, disasters by "weak" stimulus distributions as in footnote 15. N is 200 for each point on each time path, as usual in several replications (and here illustrating the conclusions of other samples and experiments as well).

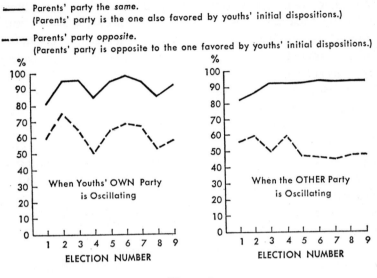

—— Parents' party the *same*.
(Parents' party is the one also favored by youths' initial dispositions.)

— — — Parents' party *opposite*.
(Parents' party is opposite to the one favored by youths' initial dispositions.)

Figure 4

Youths' vote for their *own* party, that is, the party favored by their initial disposition.

the person to vote contrary to his disposition, and for the party he normally would have low probability of choosing. In that event, the influencer seldom sees an *instance* of the choice he wants to reward and reinforce. It is like trying to reinforce an animal in behavior for what he does not do in the first place (enough to "catch" and reward). Here, however, when the appeal of the influencer's cause is made extraordinarily strong from time to time, as when a Roosevelt runs, then a large number of unusual votes for that party arise, in this model either as the youth's own first impression or in his rechecks with reality during disagreement. The influencer thus has *instances to reward*—something to work with and encourage.

Next, consider the opposite case, when parents or other influencers agree with the youth's own party inclinations. In that event, parents play a subsidiary role, because he is a "good boy" and votes their way most of the time by inner disposition. But suppose we introduce great variability in the strength of "temptations" offered the youth by the other party. Then the parent or influencer has more deviant *instances to correct*—which he can in this case because dispositions are in his favor. Again he has something to work with.

As animal experimenters and trainers of animal acts know, it is nice to have a good "random animal" who will more often display the unusual behavior one wishes to reinforce. And as every householder knows, one sometimes wishes a pet would display some unusual but obnoxious behavior more often, for example crossing a dangerous street, so that corrections could be administered and learning influenced. In politics, the same kind of opportunities may be produced by wide variations in the strength of external stimuli for the party opposite that which dispositions favor. For that will produce a richer variety of deviant behavior to correct or reinforce *selectively*.

The New Deal's rise and fall, for example, was the time to influence Republican youth and Eisenhower's rise and fall the time to influence Democratic youth—both for *and* against the cause in question—if this hypothesis applies in the real world. And if so, an unobvious implication follows. It is that compelling variations in the strength of objective stimuli from external sources can lead not to a less but a *more* decisive influence of the immediate social environment. For, a counterpart of animal variability that gives an experimenter rich opportunities for selective reinforcement is unusual variability in the deviant "temptations" that give the social environment rich opportunities to encourage or discourage selectively.

9. CONCLUSION

Serious analysis of the implications remains to be done, however, and purpose here has only been, to repeat, to illustrate a process that can reproduce the kind of "sociological" correlations found in voting and choice data, but not at the expense of the primary determinants of the choice: external stimulus and internal disposition. The portion of the model that accomplishes this can be interpreted as "selective reinforcement," but we have chosen to emphasize a less behavioristic interpretation which instead takes the point of view of the influencee. He is simply *cross-checking* impressions obtained from objective and "social reality" with one another, as all of us have to resort to doing in ambiguous situations.

The consequences at the aggregate level of social significance are generally not repugnant. Influence, and thereby tradition, counts when one has nothing else to go by—as in socialization prior to experience. Otherwise, influence is effective in this model only when it is facilitating something else, inner convictions to resist or compelling stimuli to change. If the real world is like this, it makes both sociological *and* rational sense.

Technical Note

As the Introduction said, this is an example of a process that is simple enough—alone—to be tractable in formal analysis; but it illustrates the value of doing the (easy) computer simulation first, namely, as working theory to discover what is *worth* the (difficult) formal proof. This note is to sketch how one could attack the latter, in the hope it will get the serious work this paper suggests it warrants.

Let p be the probability of voting for the cause with which the other person *disagrees* (the other's choice for the moment being fixed). Then $p + q = 1$, where q is the probability of voting for the cause with which the other would agree. Now, if the latter (type q) choice is realized, there is no disagreement in the first place, no reconsideration, and thus no chance to persist in the disagreeable choice; but if the former (p) choices comes up, there is. So, if we let $P(p;k)$ be the probability of *persisting* in the choice disagreeable to the other even after k reconsiderations,[20] it is

$$P(p;0) = p$$
$$P(p;1) = p(p) = p^2$$
$$P(p;2) = p(p^2) = p^3$$
$$\cdot$$
$$\cdot$$
$$\cdot$$
$$P(p;k) = p^{k+1}$$

$$(1)$$

A few examples give the flavor of how sensitively all this depends on p, that is, on the *strength* of the inner disposition whose manifestation is now disagreeable to others. For example, with

---

20. A "reconsideration" is a new exposure to stimulation after social disagreement with the outcome of the previous stimulation. In the foregoing paper, we permitted only one, $k = 1$, for each pair of persons (but a person could be involved in many different pairs interacting in other problems).

one reconsideration:

If $p = .20$, then $P(p;1) = (.20)^2 = .04$, or $\frac{1}{5}$ of p alone
If $p = .50$, then $P(p;1) = (.50)^2 = .25$, or $\frac{1}{2}$ of p alone
If $p = .80$, then $P(p;1) = (.80)^2 = .64$, or $\frac{4}{5}$ of p alone

Now consider why the influence also depends sensitively on the strength of stimuli. Without going into details of the stimulation process that is discussed in "Note on a Campaign Simulator" in this volume, the gist of the latter is that strong stimuli make for a *manifestation* of p with conditional probability p' that is substantially larger than p where p is moderate or small, for example, at .50 and .20 in the above example. So, if $p' > p$, then $(p')^2 \gg p^2$. Then people persist much better in their choices disagreeable to others. By the same stimulation process, when weak stimuli are present, the manifestation of p is a conditional, probably $p' < p$. Especially, p' is smaller where p is moderate or small. Then, since $p' < p$, it will be $(p')^2 \ll p^2$, and people will not persist well in the disagreeable choice.

Next, note how the number of considerations matters. Suppose people were equally distributed over all p values. Then the *total* number of contrary choices when there are 1, 2, . . . , k reconsiderations permitted would be, in contrast to no reconsiderations,

No reconsideration: $\displaystyle\int_0^1 p \, dp = \frac{1}{2}$

One reconsideration: $\displaystyle\int_0^1 p^2 \, dp = \frac{1}{3}$

$$ \tag{2} $$

Two reconsiderations: $\displaystyle\int_0^1 p^3 \, dp = \frac{1}{4}$

$k - 1$ reconsiderations: $\displaystyle\int_0^1 p^k \, dp = \frac{1}{k+1}$

Now, consider that people are not equally distributed over all p. Then the bimodal populations found in politics would make people *resistant* to influence, while the normally distributed populations found for other attitudes would make people *vulnerable*. The reason is that the number of choices changed is the initial proportion of disagreement minus the probability of persisting in that disagreement unchanged. With one reconsideration, it is

$$\text{Number of changes} = p - p^2 \qquad (3)$$

which reaches its maximum (derivative zero) at $p = \frac{1}{2}$, or where normal distribution would be dense.

Next, let the other person's choice no longer be fixed. If we let p_i and p_j be their respective probabilities of choosing one alternative, then q_i and q_j are the respective probabilities of choosing the other. Now let A $(p;k)$ be the probability they will *agree* on the p-type choice when k reconsiderations are permitted. It is for $k = 1$, one reconsideration as in the voting model:

$$\begin{aligned} A\ (p;1) &= p_i p_j + p_i q_j p_i p_j + q_i p_j p_i p_j \\ &= p_i p_j (1 + p_i q_j + q_i p_j) \end{aligned} \qquad (4a)$$

Since the expression in parenthesis would usually be much greater than 1.0, there is a good deal more *consensus* "in a world of reconsideration" than without it (where it would be $p_i p_j$ alone). And yet, choice being made by individuals in the light of their own dispositions (p), it is not an intolerable consensus. Indeed, since the chance of agreeing on the q-type choice is symmetrical,

$$A\ (q;1) = q_i q_j (1 + p_i q_j + q_i p_j) \qquad (4b)$$

with the expression in parenthesis the same as above, it depends only on $p_i p_j$ versus $q_i q_j$ which alternative is finally agreed upon. Thus, the decision satisfies the higher average disposition; for example, if one "really" wants his choice, the other gives in. But it also has the desirable property of a "built-in veto," for, no matter how high p_i is, if p_j is near zero, the joint probability is effectively the latter.

If we let any number, k, of reconsiderations take place until agreement, it is then a model of the problem when people *have* to agree finally on a common choice, for example, a television program they will all watch or an automobile purchased for common use. The algebra then becomes formidable and has only been investigated far enough to suggest it will fall into a sum of geometric series. But Ithiel Pool and Howard Raifa suggest that we already know the sums involved, on the following grounds. Suppose that agreement finally comes at the kth trial, where k is as large as we please. In theory, at least, the formal process has no "memory," no more than dice do. Therefore, the probability that the p type will win at time k, given that someone does win, is

$$A(p; k) = \frac{p_i p_j}{p_i p_j + q_i q_j}$$

the same as the conditional probability that the p type will win at *any* time, if one indeed does win.

Natural Exposure and the Theory of Popularity

3

This paper[1] first presents a model of "exposure" processes, for example, people's exposure to information about new books being published. It then analyzes the implications for "popularity" rankings, for example, the best-seller lists.

The connection between the two topics in fields like mass communications and popular culture will become apparent below; but the two problems, exposure and popularity, are much more general than our examples, which will be drawn from mass culture. In other fields the logic of each might apply independently of the other. For instance, exposure processes taken alone occur in all

1. I am indebted to Albert Madansky for the key idea in the solution in the Technical Note; to John Gilbert for clarifications that proved critical; and to the Center for Advanced Study in the Behavioral Sciences for access to such help and for my own time to complete the model. Harry Milholland was of major help on earlier computer versions, and Anthony Oberschall, Jack Ferguson, and Catherine Holbrook were helpful in various ways. This work was begun under general grants from the Ford Foundation and the National Science Foundation, G# 13045.

fields: the personal experiences by which we learn different aspects of another's personality, the samples of work performance by which a superior learns about subordinates in a large organization, and the contacts by which different ethnic groups or national citizenries form impressions of one another. Problems like popularity are similarly general in other guises: ranks of participation in small groups, word frequencies in linguistics, and ranks by city sizes in demography.

The two topics are accordingly developed in separate sections below: Part 1 on the exposure model and Part 2 on popularity. The nonmathematical reader will find it sufficient (but necessary) to understand only the notation and general ideas of the first in order to follow the substantive results in the second. The burden of our own combined argument will be, however, that when the model is interpreted as mass communications, problems in exposure to information and the abuses of popularity are as connected as, say, a celebrity and his publicity man.

1. NATURAL EXPOSURE

Commenting on what is perhaps the most fundamental difference between learning from communications in the real world and learning in laboratory experiments, Lazarsfeld has called the real-life processes like

. . . a learning experiment in which people walk in and out as they please, where some of the most valuable effects are achieved on people who come in by mere accident.[2]

That is, what is taken as "given" in laboratory experiments— not only in learning theory, but in all kinds of choice and decision problems as well—is precisely what in adult social communi-

2. In "Foreword" to J. Klapper, *The Effects of the Mass Media*, in its 1949 version as a report to the Public Library Commission, New York Bureau of Applied Social Research (mimeo).

cations is usually problematic: whether exposure to the stimulus will occur. That is, will there even be any effective *contact* with the information that is supposed to be learned or with the alternatives that could later be chosen, in the first place? This is not a problem for psychological theory, of course, but until it is covered by some theory, the overwhelming source of variance in the real outcome is not under intellectual control. And no wonder it is not, considering the complexity. For example, to continue the above quotation:

> The influences of the environment are randomly distributed among people and over time. Among the tens of thousands of men and women who can and do hear symphony programs, there are a few who are in a receptive mood at any one time.
> And even that would not happen, if at some previous time they had not happened to pick up a biography of a composer in a lending library, or if someone had not told them about an interesting and pertinent article in a popular magazine.

One could call this the problem of "natural learning," natural as distinct from the enforced exposure of the laboratory or schoolroom; but since problems like this are far more general than learning, for example, as in exposure to accidents, potential marriage partners, or whatever, call it the problem of "natural exposure" generally.

Note that in accounts of such problems, as above, there are clearly two different origins of the chaotic variance in the outcome. There are not only the different *persons* in different circumstances and moods, by which the sociologist tends to explain exposure, but also different stimulus *items* having different degrees of access in libraries, magazines, and the like. These are what the advertiser, for example, uses to explain exposure. We start with the accessibility of the latter items of information first, then deal with their reception by the people being exposed, and finally incorporate the two complements in one combined model.

a. *Alternative Stimuli*

Let the universe of information on a topic, or experiences one could have with a subject, be classified into 1, 2, 3, . . . , n different categories. These could be, for example, the 1, 2, . . . , n different aspects of another's personality with which one could become familiar in chance contacts with him. But to motivate the later analysis of popularity, we will hereafter call such categories the *alternatives:* items that could become popular if known— for example, the titles of new books that could perhaps become best-sellers if publicized. Whatever the interpretation, attached to each such item or category of information, the ith, for example, are the following theoretic chances:

p_i = probability that ith alternative will occur (here be learned) on any *one* exposure

$q_i = 1 - p_i$ = probability that it will *not* occur on any one such exposure

P_i = accumulative probability that (corresponding to expected proportion of population for whom) ith alternative will finally have occurred after *all* exposures, that is, at end of period observed

$Q_i = 1 - P_i$ = probability or expected proportion who will *not* have encountered (learned) this alternative after all exposures

The latter two accumulative probabilities will be taken as *observables;* for example, we can determine how many people know each alternative from a survey after the exposure period. It is conceivable, however, that the former probabilities on each trial could be determined by experiment, for example, by testing one trial and using the formulas below to calculate the prospects for cumulative results in subsequent real applications.

While different alternatives have different probabilities, that is, $p_i \neq p_j$, generally, we assume each p is constant over all exposures for the relevant period. So, if we know that some people had exactly x exposures, then, conditional on that fact, indicated by the notation on the left below, assume that

$$Q_i|x = q_i{}^x$$
$$P_i|x = 1 - q_i{}^x \tag{1}$$

or, on the right, that each exposure (trial) is independent of the previous one and thus, for example, the chances of failing both times when $x = 2$ exposures is $q \cdot q = q^2$.

Now, the q's for the alternatives all being less than 1.0, all would eventually go to zero and thus all the alternatives finally be learned—*if* people received sufficiently large numbers, x, of exposures—but in real life, people don't. Therefore, the significance of the size of the p's and q's is to determine on how *few* exposures a given item of information will be learned. For, in an imperfect world in which people learn little about a given subject, items of information that are not learned on few exposures are seldom learned at all.

Another way to put the technical point is in terms of "interrupted waiting time." By "waiting time" is meant the expected number of exposure trials one would have to wait before a given alternative item of information occurred and was learned. Texts on probability[3] show this expected "wait" is

$$E(x) = \frac{q_i}{p_i} \tag{2}$$

that is, the expected number of unsuccessful exposures required before i is successful (here i learned). Table 1 illustrates how in mass communications, most people "won't wait that long."

The domain of information we happen to use for illustration in Table 1, and subsequently, is knowledge about a National Broadcasting Company weekend radio service, "Monitor." For

---

3. William Feller, *An Introduction to Probability Theory and Its Applications* (Second Edition, New York: Wiley, 1957), p. 210.

Table 1

Expected "Waiting Time," in Exposures, before Alternatives Would Be Known to Half the Audience

Announcer	$E(x) = \dfrac{q_i}{p_i}$
David Brinkley ($p = .126$)	6.9
Frank Gallop ($p = .095$)	9.5
Hugh Downs ($p = .077$)	12.0
Frank Blair ($p = .065$)	14.4
Mel Brandt ($p = .052$)	18.2
Al Collins ($p = .034$)	27.6
David Russell ($p = .030$)	32.3
Gene Hamilton ($p = .025$)	39.0
Estimated exposure of actual audience:	
Median	4.0
Mean	9.0

various reasons, the best indicator of knowledge for our purposes is familiarity with the personnel staffing the service, as shown by answers to this question asked of listeners some months after the program began:

[Here is] a list of the people on Monitor. For each tell me if you ever remember listening to him.[4]

We use as the "alternatives" eight studio announcers staffing the service in relays. For while some have since become celebrities on television, at the time (1955) they were least likely to have become known by other means among listeners to this NBC service itself, the population questioned.

The point of the example is, while the median number of exposures of these listeners was only about four, and the mean at best nine, exposures, it would have taken nearly 40 exposures for the majority to know the least accessible alternatives.

4. From F. Bourne and W. McPhee, *Monitor*, an unpublished study of the Bureau of Applied Social Research, Columbia University, 1955. The basic data of relevance here are given in Table T-1 of the Technical Note ($N = 209$).

b. The Receiving Population

We know, however, that people differ from one another in interest in any one subject and in the exposure of each person to different subjects. In our model of the persons being exposed, to which we now turn, there are two sources of variation between individuals in the amount of exposure each gets: (1) an accidental component, for example, "circumstances," and (2) a systematic component, for example, "motivation."

We portray the *accidental* component by assumptions like these for a subgroup that is otherwise homogeneous in the systematic respect:

1. Exposure is a discrete event that can happen to anyone in this homogeneous group at any time, like an accident.

2. Exposure can then happen again next time to another person, or to no one, or to this same person by chance time and again.

3. Therefore, while the theoretic probability is the same for everyone in this homogeneous group and constant over time,

4. Actual results accumulated by the end of the observed period will differ widely for individuals, some having been bypassed completely while exposure events piled up on others.

The different outcomes in point 4 above—the fact that equal opportunities in theory have *un*equal outcomes in practice—is ideally described by the Poisson distribution. This distribution is approximated by so many social phenomena—even though none meet its strict conditions as described loosely above—that every social scientist who has ever counted how many people received 0 of something, how many 1, how many 2, and so, whether it is (unplanned) children or injuries or whatever "just happens naturally," has seen empirical counterparts of the Poisson distribution. Let

X = cumulated number of exposures a particular individual gets, where it can be $X = 0, 1, 2, \ldots,$
$x, \ldots, \infty$

$P(X = x) =$ probability that he will get, or expected proportion of the population who will get, exactly x exposures by the end of the observed period

$$m = \text{mean of } X = \frac{\text{total exposures}}{\text{number of people}}$$

Then the expected distribution for the proportions who get 0, 1, 2, . . . , x . . . exposures, under random conditions like those described above, can be shown to be the Poisson distribution:

$$P(X = 0) = e^{-m} \tag{3}$$
$$P(X = 1) = e^{-m}m \tag{4}$$
$$P(X = 2) = e^{-m}\frac{m^2}{2!}$$

$$\cdot$$
$$\cdot$$
$$\cdot$$

$$P(X = x) = e^{-m}\frac{m^x}{x!} \tag{5}$$

The property of the Poisson process that is most relevant here is not only an *in*equality of exposure that results from equal opportunity (equal probabilities). It is also that if we increase the amount of exposure in an effort to reduce inequality, by reaching everyone, the disparity between people in exposure increases! In fact, a measure of this disparity is the variance of the distribution of $P(X = 0)$, $P(X = 1)$, . . . , and that variance is

$$\text{var}[P(X = x)] = m$$

or the mean density of exposure itself. As in the famous Cincinnati experiment on informing people about the United Nations, efforts to reduce disparity of information between people can easily *increase* it.[5]

5. Surveys, taken before and after a trial campaign flooding the test city of Cincinnati with information on the United Nations showed that, if anything, this increased the disparity in information between the informed and uniformed. See Shirley A. Star and Helen M. Hughes, "Report of an Educational Campaign: The Cincinnati Plan for the United Nations," *American Journal of Sociology*, LV, 389–400, 1950.

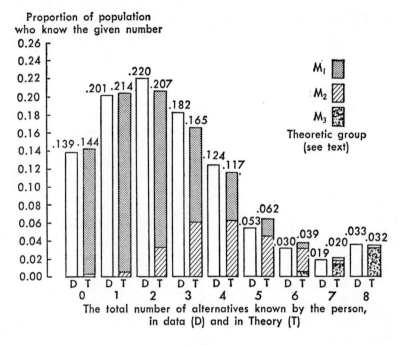

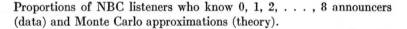

Proportion of population who know the given number

The total number of alternatives known by the person, in data (D) and in Theory (T)

Figure 1

Proportions of NBC listeners who know 0, 1, 2, . . . , 8 announcers (data) and Monte Carlo approximations (theory).

Figure 1 illustrates a typical Poisson form of distribution. The data show how many people in the audience mentioned before, of the NBC radio service, knew 0, knew 1, knew 2, and so on, of the service's announcers. The latter are only indicators of exposure and not direct measures of X, of course. Instead, X and m must be solved for a unobservables by means discussed below; but the distribution is Poissonlike, except for "the bump on the tail." This "bump" is a sign of differences in the population (for example, special fans of the NBC program versus the general public), to which we now turn as the *systematic* source of variance in amount of exposure.

Let a population consist of subproportions, M_1, M_2, M_3, . . . , differing in that they have different mean densities of exposure, m_1, m_2, m_3, . . . , as a result of different probabilities of exposure at any one time, on an average among people of the different types. "On an average" is important, however, because an individual in the more densely exposed type may nevertheless happen by circumstances himself to get little or no exposure. Indeed, even if m_2 is vastly larger than m_1—in our radio example, the former is three times as large as the latter—nevertheless, it is predictable from the Poisson process that an occasional individual of the M_2 type will get almost no exposure, while an occasional M_1 type will get a dozen! This expresses the truth that, for example, careful people do have accidents and careless people do go accident-free. Rather what we mean by "careful" and "careless" are expected averages, m_1, m_2, and m_3.

Again the m's and M's must be solved for as unobservables, and for this reason we use the minimum necessary to fit the data, here three, so that, with the names of the types standing for their respective proportions of the population,

$$M_1 + M_2 + M_3 = 1 \qquad (6)$$

Illustrative are the solutions we get for the radio data, roughly

$$M_1 = .70 \qquad M_2 = .25 \qquad M_3 = .05$$
$$m_1 = 4 \qquad m_2 = 12 \qquad m_3 = 65$$

On the left is a large group of "general public" with moderate exposure, in the center a smaller group of "fans" with much exposure, and on the right a very few "gluttons" for this fare. The *unit* of exposure, what the exposure event "is," is a theoretic idea, but in the case of our example, there is independent evidence that it roughly parallels the number of different weekends people had heard the radio service in the half a year or so it had been running. Because of the latter limits, the m_3 estimate is suspect. A note explains a different process probably at work there.[6]

c. The Combined Model

The two models now go together in a complementary way. For, the Poisson process gives the exposure, but not its outcome. The earlier binomial process for learning alternatives gives the outcome, but the exposure must be supplied. Within one homogenous group, M, the two now combine happily, in either of two forms for the occurrence of alternative i,

$$P \ (x \text{ and } i) = e^{-m} \frac{m^x}{x!} (1 - q_i{}^x) \qquad (\text{``Tandem''}) \qquad (7)$$

$$P \ (i, x \text{ times}) = e^{-mp_i} \frac{(mp_i)^x}{x!} \qquad (\text{``Compound''}) \qquad (8)$$

where the notation on the left means in the upper case, "the probability of x exposures and i occurs on any of them," while in the lower case it is, "the probability that i occurs x times."

The latter is a *repetition* concept that would be important in learning problems; formally, it is the "compound" Poisson process. The other form on the upper row tells whether the alternative occurs *at all*. Because of its unorthodox form, we dub it the "tandem" combination; but it incorporates the same assumptions, and we use the two forms interchangeably as one model.

Consider the so-called "zero" term of the compound Poisson, the probability that alternative i will not occur at all. In our

6. The main reason it takes so much exposure to reproduce what M_3 people report knowing (seven or eight of eight alternatives) is that in this model each exposure event is independent of the previous ones and thus their outcomes tend to *duplicate*—the same alternatives keep occurring that people already know rather than the last one or two small items they did not know. But in real life, M_3-type people are shut-ins and the like who expose themselves not in discrete events but in great serial blocs; for example listen to "Monitor" all weekend, in which case the stimulus items occur nonrandomly, since all the NBC announcers come on in a serial schedule (but see also Note 17 for defects in the data).

model it is, substituting the mp_i of expression (8) above for the m of expression (3), as follows:

$$P \ (i, \ 0 \ \text{times}) \ = \ M_1 e^{-m_1 p_i} + M_2 e^{-m_2 p_i} + M_3 e^{-m_3 p_i} \qquad (9)$$

where we now show the complete version for three different M groups and make the essential assumption that p_i is the same in all groups. This expression (9) is crucial in estimating parameters, for it is equivalent to an easily observed quantity, Q_i, or the proportion who have *not* learned the alternative (for example, as determined in a survey after the period in question). Unfortunately, expression (9) cannot be solved explicitly in this form, and it is convenient to find special situations in which only one of the groups of terms on the right is effectively not zero. The Technical Note shows that, if we define Q_{hijk} as the observed failure to know *any* of alternatives h, i, j, and k, this observed quantity is equivalent to

$$Q_{hijk} = M_1 e^{-m_1(1 - q_h q_i q_j q_k)} + \cdots \qquad (10)$$

where we indicate on the far right that, in theory, there would be additional terms analogous to the first (which gives the contribution only of the lightly exposed, or M_1, group); but these other terms, in a special case, can be neglected as virtually zero. The case we take for solutions concerns the top few alternatives, who are known to nearly a majority of all kinds of people. Thus *not* knowing *any* of the top three or four, the "obvious" alternatives, is scarcely expectable of the "fans" in M_2 or the "gluttons" in M_3. A few fans, who might still be expected to be so ignorant, are what are neglected on the right above. Other simplifying assumptions would suit other data, but this will certainly be a common one (indicated when a single Poisson will fit lower but not higher ranges of knowledge, the case here).

If so, taking every combination of items appropriate to simplications like (10), and converting to natural logarithms,

$$\log Q_{hijk} - \log M_1 + m_1 = m_1 q_h q_i q_j q_k \qquad (11)$$

we can subtract any two such expressions to eliminate M_1 and the m_1 on the left. Then, taking the results of two such subtractions suitably chosen, we can form a ratio of those, in turn, that has the convenient form

$$\frac{\log Q_{i,j,k} - \log Q_{i,j,k,h}}{\log Q_{j,k} - \log Q_{j,k,h}} = \frac{m_1 q_i q_j q_k (1 - q_h)}{m_1 q_j q_k (1 - q_h)} = q_i \qquad (12)$$

and thus estimates of parameters like q_i are determined by logarithms of observables on the left. In practice, these give only first approximations, which must be improved iteratively; and the mathematical reader is referred to the Technical Note for the need for more efficient statistical methods to develop this as a measurement model, as it indeed is (a measure of "underlying exposure").

The challenge for further mathematical work is also indicated by the theoretic "calculations" used to match examples of real data for our illustrations. The Technical Note shows how to derive an explicit formula for every quantity shown; but one would have to be motivated by a serious application, important data, to calculate the great number of permutations and combinations that present formulas require. Pending mathematical simplification (which seems hopeful), we use for present illustrative purposes a much simpler and more intuitive Monte Carlo procedure. It also serves to show the simplicity of the model for nonmathematical readers, namely, to fit our radio example:

1. A sample of 1000 "people" was divided into our estimated numbers of M_1, M_2, and M_3, respectively, 700, 250, and 50 people.

2. Since the mean densities of exposure in each group were estimated to be 4, 12, and 65, respectively, 2,800, 3,000, and 3,250 exposure events were administered to individuals chosen at random each time within the respective groups.

3. Given an exposure "event" for the person, it consisted of a set of n trials, here $n = 8$, each determining independently of the others whether a given alternative was learned, that is,

Table 2

Proportion of Population Who Know Alternative *i* and *k* in

Total = P (k and i)ᵃ

And Know Alternative *i*		Total known, *k*							
		1	2	3	4	5	6	7	8
1. Brinkley:	Actual:	.062	.115	.125	.105	.048	.024	.019	.033
	Theory:	.064	.094	.123	.093	.059	.037	.020	.032
2. Gallop:	Actual:	.038	.101	.100	.081	.043	.029	.019	.033
	Theory:	.040	.091	.098	.091	.058	.032	.020	.032
3. Downs:	Actual:	.038	.058	.101	.076	.029	.014	.019	.033
	Theory:	.033	.061	.074	.074	.041	.038	.020	.032
4. Blair:	Actual:	.034	.062	.057	.076	.034	.015	.014	.033
	Theory:	.026	.052	.065	.066	.045	.036	.020	.032
5. Brandt:	Actual:	.010	.048	.077	.043	.029	.014	.014	.033
	Theory:	.016	.040	.043	.054	.036	.029	.018	.032
6. Collins:	Actual:	.010	.029	.024	.033	.029	.024	.019	.033
	Theory:	.009	.030	.038	.037	.028	.021	.017	.032
7. Russell:	Actual:	.005	.019	.034	.029	.038	.029	.014	.033
	Theory:	.015	.027	.032	.029	.022	.018	.012	.032
8. Hamilton:	Actual:	.005	.010	.029	.053	.014	.024	.014	.033
	Theory:	.011	.019	.022	.024	.021	.023	.013	.032

a. The table entry is P (k and i) referred to later, the probability that k alternatives are known and these include i. N is 209, actual, 1,000 theory (Monte Carlo).

whether a random number fell within an interval defining its probability.[7]

These procedures (in a computer) would be more convenient when n is significantly greater than about 10 alternatives. It turns

7. We have not emphasized the assumption made explicit here that the outcomes, for example, the items of information, occur independently of one another. For, this is but one version of the model. Other versions would be appropriate to different applications, for example, one might want the outcomes to be mutually exclusive in any one exposure event. The last would replace procedure 3 above with the drawing of a single random number that would identify which alternative occurred. (As John Gilbert suggested, this leads to different results for m small, for example, m_1, virtually the same for m large, such as m_3.) Our independence assumption simply happens to be the one for which parameter solutions have been developed thus far.

out that exact calculations would actually have been less time-consuming for our own case of $n < 10$, as the reader will see in the explicit expressions of the Technical Note; but we use the intuitive Monte Carlo data in the main text as illustration that the formidable-looking notation is only that and is no bar to practical use.

The fit[8] that can be obtained from such procedures, prior to serious work on the mathematical statistics of this as an inductive (measurement) model, is illustrated in Table 2. In the remaining text, we deal with its deductive implications as a theory.

2. THE THEORY OF POPULARITY

It seems a contradiction to discuss the implications of a particular model and yet speak of "the" theory of popularity generally (that is, *any* ranking by popular renown or public choices). It is true this model is appropriate only to cases where public exposure to the alternatives is important in popularity, for example, as publicity is in best-seller rankings, exposure to the music is for the "top ten" tunes, and the like. After seeing the implications to follow, however, most readers will agree that the same consequences could be found in many other cases where the elementary mechanisms would surely not be the same as the exposure processes above. Evidence of this generality from other work, for example, from that in small groups, will be discussed. Thus, there is promise of a general *logic* of popularity that transcends the content of particular models like this one, which calls attention to it.

The ideas that the present model adds to the general discussion are given below under the rubrics of (a) "natural weighting,"

8. Actually, we have not taken the trouble for these trivial illustrations to show the best fit that can be obtained by repeating the Monte Carlo after refining the parameter estimates, for example adjusting the p's for individual alternatives exactly to fit their marginals, scaling m_2 down somewhat to fit exactly in Figure 1, and the like, which a serious application would warrant by means discussed in the Technical Note.

(b) "natural monopoly," (c) a naturally-occurring form of "double jeopardy," and (d) certain "natural distributions" others have found in popularity data. The word "natural" means not "laws" of nature, but that unless humans intervene with more sensible arrangements, the following will happen.

a. Natural Weighting

For most purposes, what matters is not absolute but *relative* popularity—"more," "most," "better," "best," comparatively. Yet in any voting on relative popularity (or in any "knowing" that affects relative renown), the choices of different kinds of people have different weight (Figure 2).

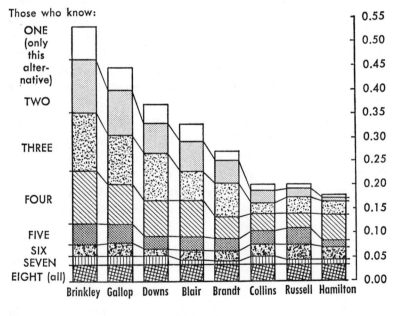

Figure 2

The composition of those who know each alternative (vertical bar) by the total number of alternatives they know (horizontal strata).

Figure 2 tabulates the number of people who know each alternative—each announcer in our example of the radio data—in the following way. Those people who know *all* alternatives (here eight) are first counted. They are shown at the bottom of each bar, the bar portraying the proportion of people who know each alternative. Notice in Figure 2 that the number of people who know all eight makes *no* difference to an alternative's *relative* popularity, or here to its relative renown, because they give the same increment to every other alternative as well. Virtually the same is true when we add those people, as an increment to each bar concerned, who know six or seven of the eight alternatives. What good is an increment to some alternative's relative renown if the people who know that alternative know most of all the other alternatives as well? "A vote for me and a vote for my competitor is no vote at all." As Figure 2 shows, it is only when we add the increment originating from people who know few alternatives, or in other applications who choose few alternatives, that the increment in renown, or choices, that they thereby give to some alternative is important—because this increment is *not* given to competitors as well.

An effect like this is sometimes created deliberately by minority political parties and dissenting stockholder factions. Allowed eight choices, say, for eight legislators or eight directors, they refrain from making most of them in order to give *relative* weight to the one or two choices they do want. To explain, suppose we are adding one such person's choice of alternative i right now to a previous tally that stands

$$\frac{\text{Total for } i\text{th alternative}}{\text{Total for all alternatives}}$$

Now, if the person makes eight choices, that adds 1 to the numerator for each alternative chosen, here the ith, but it adds 8 to the denominator. The relative increment this person adds to each is 1/8 unit. Whereas a person making but one choice of one alternative alone adds 1 to the denominator and only 1 to the numerator, Its weight is 1/1, or a full unit. Thus, different people who make 1, 2, 3, . . . , k total choices, including a given one, give each subchoice relative increments of, respectively,

$$\frac{1}{1}, \frac{1}{2}, \frac{1}{3}, \cdots, \frac{1}{k}$$

The reader for whom this is intuitive can skip to the corresponding formal result in expression (15) below, whose notation is as follows. Let the measure of "relative" renown or popularity, the "tally" shown above, be

$$\frac{P_i}{\sum\limits_{i=1}^{n} P_i} = \text{relative renown}$$

or the *share* this alternative has of all instances of knowing or choosing. Then let

$$K = \text{total number of alternatives known}$$
$$P\,(K = k) = \text{probability } k \text{ are known (or proportion who know } k)$$
$$P\,(k \text{ and } i) = \text{probability } k \text{ are known and these include } i$$

To derive the result discussed above, note that

$$\frac{P\,(k \text{ and } i)}{\sum\limits_{i=1}^{n} P\,(k \text{ and } i)}$$

is the share that i has of all instances of knowing among the subgroup of people who know k in total. We can express the total share that alternative i has among *all* people as an average of these shares in different strata by k, weighted by the number of people involved in each:

$$\frac{P_i}{\sum_{i=1}^{n} P_i} = P\,(K = 1)\,\frac{P\,(1 \text{ and } i)}{\sum_{i=1}^{n} P\,(1 \text{ and } i)}$$

$$+ P\,(K = 2)\,\frac{P\,(2 \text{ and } i)}{\sum_{i=1}^{n} P\,(2 \text{ and } i)} + \cdots \quad (13)$$

where the series continues over all k. Now, a typical one of the weights in the series, $P\,(K = k)$, can be rewritten

$$P\,(K = k) = \frac{\sum_{i=1}^{n} P\,(k \text{ and } i)}{k} \quad (14)$$

because the numerator is the total number of instances of knowing; and dividing by the k instances per person in this group gives the number of people involved, the weight. Substituting this for the weight in a typical term of (13), we obtain

$$\cdots + \left[\frac{\sum_{i=1}^{n} P\,(k \text{ and } i)}{k}\right] \frac{P\,(k \text{ and } i)}{\sum_{i=1}^{n} P\,(k \text{ and } i)} + \cdots$$

The Σ expressions cancel in all such terms. So, relative renown is a simple sum:

$$\frac{P_i}{\sum_{i=1}^{n} P_i} = \frac{P\,(1 \text{ and } i)}{1} + \frac{P\,(2 \text{ and } i)}{2} + \frac{P\,(3 \text{ and } i)}{3} + \cdots$$

$$= \sum_{k=1}^{n} P\,(k \text{ and } i)\,\frac{1}{k} \quad (15)$$

The weight for each term in this sum, $1/k$, diminishes very rapidly in the first few terms, 1.00, 0.50, 0.33, 0.25, ... Thus, usually these very first few terms are what matter. So, consider *whom* they represent, here in terms of their knowledge (number of items known), in other applications their participation (number of choices made).

The small k, which gets the sharply higher weight, $1/1$, or $1/2$, means by definition that the people involved *know* little, only one or two of all the n items of information or alternatives others know. The *less* they know, the *more* the weight given to each thing they do know. Therefore, when a procedure adopted by dissenting stockholders and minority political parties "happens naturally," as it does here in popular renown, it is not the choices of an intense minority that are being given maximum weight, but those of a mass of people *marginal* to a field.

The difference between the weight given a choice by a marginal person who makes only one choice and the weight given to a choice of a person who makes a large number, k, is easily obtained by subtraction:

$$\frac{1}{1} - \frac{1}{k} = \frac{k-1}{k} \tag{16}$$

The right term is a measure of "dilution"—the potential weight of a choice dissipated by making other choices as well. And the point is that it is a dilution of precisely the preferences we would like weighted *most*, those of people who participate most and thus know most.[9]

It would seem there is one consolation, however. Those who dilute the weight of what they know or choose, because they know or choose "too much," at least give their diluted weights to more alternatives. For while it is true that those who know or choose

9. An opposite value judgment can be made in some cases, for example, in the television ratings. There one might wish that the marginal viewer, who is typically male, mature, and college-educated, *were* indeed weighted equally with the heavy television consumer, typically less-educated women and children.

k alternatives give each only a $1/k$th increment, this process is repeated k times for that many different alternatives. Therefore, would not everyone have the same weight in *total*, $k (1/k) = 1$? Actually, even if so, this would be small consolation in the best-seller rankings, say, if the keenest student of current literature, who buys 100 books a year, had the same weight as somebody who casually buys, as a gift, the one and only book he has heard about all year. Unfortunately, the situation seems worse than that, although we can only sketch the formal argument.

Consider the relative *difference* between two alternatives in their shares of renown:

$$\frac{P_i - P_j}{\sum\limits_{i=1}^{n} P_i} = \sum_{k=1}^{n} [P \ (k \text{ and } i) - P(k \text{ and } j)] \frac{1}{k} \qquad (17)$$

obtained by simply subtracting the two sums (15) for each. Next consider the contribution to this difference in a typical term by people who know k alternatives. It is divided below by the number of such people, $P \ (K = k)$, to arrive at the contribution *per person*:

$$\left[\frac{P \ (k \text{ and } i) - P \ (k \text{ and } j)}{P \ (K = k)} \right] \frac{1}{k} \qquad (18)$$

Next, recall from elementary probability that

$$P \ (k \text{ and } i) = P \ (K = k) \ P \ (i;k) \qquad (19)$$

where $P \ (i;k)$ is the conditional probability of knowing i, if k in total are known. Substituting (19) in (18) and noticing that the $P \ (K = k)$ terms cancel, we have the contribution per person (to differences in renown) among people at the kth level of information:

$$\frac{P \ (i;k) - P \ (j;k)}{k} \qquad (20)$$

Now consider an analogous expression for better informed people who know *more* on this topic, for instance, those who know $k + 1$ items. Let the different probabilities for them be expressed by

$$P (i;k + 1) = P (i;k) + a_k$$
$$P (j;k + 1) = P (j;k) + a_k + b_k$$

(21)

where a_k and b_k are positive increments, with a_k an increase in the probability that i will be known now that $k + 1$ are known. In the case of alternative j, the additional $b_k > 0$ expresses the fact developed in the next section, that *on an average* the conditional probability of knowing the *lesser* alternative, j, increases even more than the probability of i, with increments in k.[10]

Therefore, if we substitute $k + 1$ for k to obtain an expression for the contribution by people who know $k + 1$ alternatives, analogous to expression (20) above, we now have the contribution to the difference in renown of alternatives by people who are better-informed—as in the minimum case here, those who know $k + 1$ items of information as opposed to k in (20) above,

$$\frac{P (i;k + 1) - P (j;k + 1)}{k + 1} = \frac{[P (i;k) + a_k] - [P (j;k) + a_k + b_k]}{k + 1}$$

$$= \frac{P (i;k) - P (j;k) - b_k}{k + 1}$$

(22)

The last row suggests that $k + 1$ people contribute *less* than k people, for it is less than the corresponding result in expression (20) on two counts: First, $1/(k + 1)$ is less than $1/k$, particularly where k is small. And second, the numerator in the second case is usually smaller by the factor b_k, particularly with k large.

Thus, to come back to the example earlier of the person who buys or knows 100 new books being given no more weight than the person who knows or buys only one, in each's total contribution to relative renown of books; the actual facts are probably even worse. For in each person's contribution to the *differences* in

10. See Table 4 and its discussion. This is not true for *all i, j, k.*

renown that make a best-seller "best," we get a smaller weight the more that people know, from k to $k + 1$ to $k + 2$ and so on. So, unless someone can make better sense of the algebra than we,[11] this seems to be the unhappy character of "natural" weighting: the less the person participates, the more he counts.

b. Natural Monopoly

We shall use the above results shortly, but first consider an apparently different finding that has turned up over and over again in the empirical study of mass audiences. It is true by definition that the mass medium found to be the most popular attraction is the one that has recruited more people of almost all types into its audience, in raw numbers; but there seems no reason that it should also be found to have recruited the greatest relative fraction of its own audience—and thus *many more* than proportionately in raw numbers—from among people of a certain type. Technically, this is the type of person least reached by the other media covering the same topic, for example, the "unduplicated" circulation of mass media; but by that fact—that an audience is unduplicated by other material on the same topic—means it consists of people who *care* least to seek out multiple information on the topic or follow multiple attractions in this domain.

For example, in Table 3 we show the ranks in over-all popularity (circulation) of five house-and-garden type magazines.[12] Then beside each one is given the same magazine's rank as to the proportion of its subscribers who do *not* subscribe to any other house-and-garden magazine—in contrast to people especially interested in the house-and-garden field who take two or three. De-

11. These are tricky problems that we do not pretend to analyze fully in passing here but merely to call attention to work needed on them by the unhappy suggestions this model makes.

12. This example is from "The Market for Flowers," and the other two examples in Table 3 are from "Denver Post Readership Survey" and "Coors Baseball Survey," unpublished studies in the 1940s on file at Research Services, Inc., Denver, and reviewed in W. McPhee, *Inductive Reasoning in Social Research* (New York: The Free Press of Glencoe, 1963, in revision).

tailed results summarized by these ranks show that the most popular magazine gets not only more raw numbers of people of otherwise marginal participation in the field, but a *disproportionate* share of its audience (a larger fraction of its already larger circulation) consists of just such marginal people.

The phenomenon has no inherent connection to media circulation, however, as other examples in Table 2 concerning interest

Table 3

Rank in Size of Total Following of the Alternative and Its Rank in Ability to Reach People Least Reached by Other Alternatives

Rank of House-and-Garden-Type Magazines by		Rank of Editorial-Page Columns and Features by:		Rank of Sports Broadcasts by:	
Total Circulation in This Sample	Relative Proportion of Its Readers Who Do *Not* Read Others	Total Size of Following for the Feature	Relative Proportion of Its Readers Who Are *Light* Readers of Editorial Page Generally	Total Number Interested in Hearing This Sport	Relative Proportion of Those Interested in This Sport Who Are *Not* Interested in Most Popular Sport (Baseball)
1	1	1	1	1	2
2	2	2	2	2	1
3	3	3	$5\frac{1}{2}$	3	3
4	4	4	3	4	4
5	5	5	4	5	5
		6	$5\frac{1}{2}$		
		7	9		
		8	$7\frac{1}{2}$		
		9	$7\frac{1}{2}$		
		10	11		
		11	$14\frac{1}{2}$		
		12	11		
		13	13		
		14	$14\frac{1}{2}$		
		15	$16\frac{1}{2}$		
		16	11		
		17	$16\frac{1}{2}$		

in sports and in serious newspaper editorials also show. The data on editorials came from efforts to get more of the people least interested in the editorial pages to stop and read at least something there. A survey was taken to find out what sort of attraction appealed to such marginal readers. As a measure of such appeal, each existing item on the editorial pages was ranked as to the proportion of its readers recruited from people who did *not* read much else on these pages. It turned out not only that the most popular items recruited many more such readers in raw numbers, but also that a greater *relative* fraction of such a popular item's already greater number of readers was recruited from among those people who had the least interest in anything else on the editorial pages. The sports example is analogous: those least interested in sports generally were a larger proportion of the already larger audience interested in the most popular sport.

If this situation existed for some logically inherent reason, it would be a particularly unhappy result, for the most popular alternatives would have, in addition to the numerical advantage of popularity itself, a uniqueness or *monopoly* among the people least informed about this class of alternatives and thus least in a position to defend themselves against abuses of popularity. For example, readers of the most popular newspapers would be disproportionately the people who are insulated from comparisons with the accounts of other newspapers.

To see why this conclusion indeed seems inescapable, let us simply turn around the implied direction of causation in the above finding. Let it now read: The alternative that most monopolizes people who know or choose few other alternatives is *therefore* the most popular alternative. For we need recall only that the relative popularity of alternative i was a sum of different groups (proportions) of the population knowing alternative i and k in total, each such group weighted in one manner or another by how *few* alternatives they knew. The alternative is more popular because it has a uniqueness, a monopoly, among those who know or choose few competitors.

Thus, the unduplicated-audience "finding" in empirical studies is simply the natural weighting phenomenon in another guise; but it does demand new explanation. Why do *certain* alternatives have the advantage, others not, in the first place? That is, why are the weightier choices of marginal people not more random with respect to the different alternatives?

Table 4 illustrates the distinctly nonrandom pattern whereby top items—in our radio illustration, Brinkley, Gallop, and Downs—dominate much more among people who know least than among others. Monte Carlo data reproduce the same from the model, and its logic reveals why we need not invent behavioral explanations such as, "Ignorant people prefer only the popular." Instead, there are two simpler origins of the result in the natural spread of information.

The first source is the systematic heterogeneity in the population, that is, M_1, M_2, M_3, ... To explain, the weaker alternative at any one moment—for example, one not being given much publicity—has smaller p or smaller chance of being learned on a given exposure to this domain of alternatives, that is, to this topic. But that smaller p means that this alternative tends to be

Table 4

Share That the First Three Alternatives Are All Instances of Knowing Alternatives

Among People Whose Total Knowledge is k =	Proportion of All Known That Were Brinkley, Gallop, or Downs		
	Actual	Theory[a]	(N's)
One alternative	.68	.64	(42) (214)
Two alternatives	.62	.59	(46) (207)
Three alternatives	.60	.60	(38) (165)
Four alternatives	.53	.55	(26) (117)
Five alternatives	.45	.51	(11) (62)
Six alternatives	.39	.46	(6) (39)
Seven alternatives	.43	.43	(4) (20)
Eight alternatives[b]	.38	.38	(7) (32)

a. Monte Carlo. See Technical Note for the explicit combinational expression involved.
b. 0.375 by definition for both.

learned *only* by people in the groups heavily exposed to the topic, here M_2 and M_3. Table 5 below gives the expected proportion of each alternative's following recruited from the different M groups, easily calculated from a formula shown in Table 5. (Monte Carlo data are also shown as a check on them.) The weaker alternatives

Table 5

Expected Share of Each Alternative's Following Recruited From M_1, M_2, and M_3 Groups

	Those Who Know It Are[a]		
	M_1	M_2	M_3
Brinkley			
Calculated[b]	.53	.37	.10
Monte Carlo	.53	.37	.10
Gallop			
Calculated	.50	.39	.11
Monte Carlo	.53	.36	.11
Downs			
Calculated	.48	.39	.13
Monte Carlo	.49	.38	.13
Blair			
Calculated	.47	.39	.14
Monte Carlo	.47	.38	.15
Brandt			
Calculated	.45	.39	.16
Monte Carlo	.43	.39	.18
Collins			
Calculated	.40	.38	.21
Monte Carlo	.41	.37	.22
Russell			
Calculated	.40	.38	.22
Monte Carlo	.45	.34	.21
Hamilton			
Calculated	.39	.38	.23
Monte Carlo	.38	.36	.25

a. The total of $M_1 + M_2 + M_3$ is always 1.00.
b. Since $e^{-m_j p_i}$ is the proportion expected *not* to know it in any M group, the calculated data are

$$\frac{M_j(1 - e^{-m_j p_i})}{\sum_{j=1}^{3} M_j(1 - e^{-m_j p_i})}$$

are heavily dependent on the M_2 fans and M_3 gluttons for their renown; but if such heavy exposure is required to get to know a given alternative, people who get that much exposure are learning all the *other* alternatives as well. The obscure restaurant that is known only to the connoisseur, for example, is unfortunately known to the man who knows every other restaurant in town too.

The second origin of the tendency for the popular but not the unpopular alternative to monopolize the ill-informed occurs within a homogeneous group with identical probabilities of exposure in theory. It happens anyway, by accident. As a Poisson process predicts, however, this is, so to speak, no accident. Many people's exposure is, despite good theoretic chances, as if "aborted." It stops for chance reasons at some X amount far less than average, much less than potential. Now, the share that a given alternative will have of the knowledge or choices of such people depends sensitively on what X exposure they do get, namely, the expected share of alternative i is

$$\frac{(1 - q_i{}^x)}{(1 - q_1{}^x) + (1 - q_2{}^x) + \cdots + (1 - q_n{}^x)} = \frac{1 - q_i{}^x}{n - \sum_1^n q^x} \quad (23)$$

While for other people with large amounts of exposure, this fraction approaches a limit of $1/n$ share for every alternative and thus all alternatives on an equal footing, for people with minimum exposure, $X = 1$, it is $p/\Sigma p$. This situation is highly unequal, for example, completely dependent on publicity. In our radio example, it gives the most popular alternative an advantage four times as great among people with minimum exposure as it does among people with the maximum exposure.

The fact that chance events alone, without any heterogeneity in the population, nevertheless give the alternative with higher p greater uniqueness or monopoly among people with less exposure to the topic is illustrated in Table 6. Consider the average number of alternatives expected to be known, $E(k;i)$, when al-

Table 6

**Mean Number of *Other* Items Known When Item *i* Is
Known $= E(k;i) - 1$ [a]**

	In Each Group Separately			Weighted Average	Actual Data
	M_1	M_2	M_3		
Brinkley	1.7	3.0	6.5	2.7	2.5
Gallop	1.8	3.2	6.5	2.8	2.7
Downs	1.8	3.3	6.5	3.0	2.8
Blair	1.9	3.4	6.5	3.2	2.9
Brandt	2.0	3.4	6.6	3.4	3.1
Collins	2.0	3.5	6.6	3.6	3.8
Russell	1.9	3.6	6.8	3.5	3.9
Hamilton	2.1	3.7	6.7	3.9	4.1

a. The table entry is called $E(r;i)$ in formula (70) in the Technical Note, on which we place much hope for efficient solutions. For its use, the precise actual-data figures above were, respectively, 2.523, 2.720, 2.779, 2.868, 3.125, 3.786, 3.929, 4.053, whose range present parameters do not fully fit.

ternative i is known. Then subtracting one, i itself, we have the average number of *competitors* known when i is known, $E(k;i) - 1$. This is shown separately for each alternative in each M group. The systematically fewer competitive alternatives known when the top alternatives are known holds, is theoretically expected to, within each M group separately. (Except for the empirical totals, these are Monte Carlo data; but a note shows this would be tedious but not prohibitive to calculate exactly.)[13]

Thus it can be shown that the monopolylike tendency—that the weaker alternatives are at their weakest and the stronger alternatives at their strongest among people who know the *least*— is due to the unhappily reinforcing effects not only of (a) the heterogeneity of motivation to seek out unobvious alternatives, but also of (b) chance events even within a population absolutely homogenous in all such good intentions. For minimum exposure can arise either way, by motive or by chance, and minimum exposure of people leads to the same consequence in either case: a

13. By the formula for $E(r;i)$, expression (70) in the Technical Note.

"natural" tendency toward monopoly of the popular over the uninformed.

c. Double Jeopardy

A regularity called to the writer's attention by Jack Landis' intensive analyses of it, originally arose as a methodological puzzle.[14] For example, when one takes a poll of the relative appeal of movie stars or television talent, as Gallup does regularly, one can only ask "like-dislike" questions about a given attraction among people who are familiar with that attraction. The puzzling result in question is that (a) the larger the proportion of the people who are *not* familiar with this alternative, then (b) the less likely are those in the subsample who are familiar with it to *like* it especially. This seems absurd. The number of other people who have not yet become familiar with an alternative should have nothing to do with whether or not those who have become familiar with it like it. This result is so dependable that it requires a correction, whereby the conditional probability that people who know an alternative will like it must be compared with a "par" appropriate for its particular level of over-all renown or lack of renown—the less renown, the less the probability, if known, of being (especially) liked.

Two sets of our own data provide convenient illustration in Table 7. The first consists of the familiar radio example. The previous data used above were answers when people in the survey were asked to pick out personalities whom they *knew* from a list (not only the list of announcers we have been using here but of the celebrity talent on the same NBC service). Next, the interviewer requested:

Now I'll read back through the ones you've listened to, you tell me any you especially *like* . . .

14. In unpublished work at the National Broadcasting Company and J. Walter Thompson, Inc. Landis has since worked out explanations for the case of television programs, but we have not had opportunity as yet to examine their connection to the present general considerations.

Liking is not just knowing, but choosing. We have not distinguished between the two previously, because the foregoing points would apply to either knowledge or choices. But now there is a difference. Continue to call the proportion who know the alternative P_i. Then let the proportion of those people (and of only those) who further answer they "like" the alternative be the conditional probability, $P(C_i;P_i)$. The C_i means "choice," here only implicitly as "like"; but in other applications it is explicitly "like best" or "prefer," and in real life it means to choose objectively, for example, to "buy" or to "decide" among the alternatives one knows.

A third notation is necessary in Table 7 for the sequel. In real life, $P(C_i;P_i)$, the choice conditional on knowing the alternative, is *not* usually what is observed. Rather, the observable is the proportion of the whole population, call it $P(C_i)$, that chooses the alternative. But, in our data, as we now formally assume,

$$P(C_i) = P_i P(C_i;P_i) \qquad (24)$$

that is, choices of an alternative are recruited only from those who know it. For example, readers of a newspaper were asked to choose the "best three" comic strips in the paper, unconditionally; but we find from other data on readership that no one chose as best an alternative he did not read.[15] These data on comics are shown in Table 7 also. As with our radio data, the first column is P_i, in the comics data the proportion who read and thus are familiar with the comic. Then the next two columns are $P(C;P_i)$, the probability of choosing or liking conditional on (as a proportion of those) knowing the alternative, and $P(C_i)$ the final choices as a proportion of the whole population.

We will deal with the last column later, and for now the point is the remarkable *non*independence of ranks in the first two columns. This is the phenomenon that Landis noted and that we call "double jeopardy."

15. These are from a 1947 "Denver Post Readership Survey" also reviewed in the reference cited in Note 12.

Table 7

Observed Choices $P(C_i)$ as a Product of Knowledge (P_i) and Choice among Those Who Know $P(C_i;P_i)$

	Among Listeners to the Network Service		
	P_i Proportion Who Have Heard Him	$P(C_i;P_i)$ Among Hearers Only, Like Him Especially	$P(C_i)$ Total Who Like Each Especially
Celebrities:			
Dave Garroway	.92a	.64a	.59a
Bob and Ray	.86	.51	.44
Henry Morgan	.84	.59	.50
Morgan Beatty	.82	.47	.39
Ben Grauer	.78	.54	.42
Clifton Fadiman	.67	.51	.34
Walter Kiernan	.63	.57	.36
Staff:			
Brinkley	.53	.38	.20
Gallop	.44	.34	.15
Downs	.37	.30	.11
Blair	.32	.33	.11
Brandt	.27	.31	.08
Collins	.20	.25	.05
Russell	.20	.25	.05
Hamilton	.18	.32	.06

	Among Readers of the Newspaper		
	P_i Proportion Who Read the Comic Regularly	$P(C_i;P_i)$ Among Regulars Only, Rate It among the Best Three	$P(C_i)$ Total Choosing Each Among Three Best
Blondie	.83b	.53b	.44b
Dick Tracy	.78	.43	.34
Gasoline Alley	.76	.29	.22
Donald Duck	.68	.22	.15
Mutt and Jeff	.65	.17	.11
Brenda Starr	.61	.38	.23
Moon Mullins	.60	.10	.06
R. Morgan	.59	.32	.19
Orphan Annie	.59	.28	.17
Willie D.	.57	.19	.11
Mary Worth	.56	.31	.18
Barney Google	.54	.15	.08
Joe Palooka	.52	.09	.05
Steve Canyon	.50	.19	.09
Terry	.44	.14	.06
Gordo	.44	.15	.07
R. Kirby	.41	.10	.04
Mark Trail	.39	.07	.03
Peanuts	.36	.06	.07
Red Ryder	.36	.19	.03
B. Saddler	.33	.08	.02

a. Thus 64 per cent of those in the 92 per cent who have heard him like him, and these are 59 per cent of the population.
b. Thus, 53 per cent of those in the 83 per cent who read it rate it among the best, these being 44 per cent of the population.

The "jeopardy" is for the lesser-known alternative. The reason it is "double" is this: On top of the initial disadvantage (1) that such an unpublicized alternative is unknown to many people, who therefore *cannot* choose it, there is a second disadvantage (2) that the few people who do know the lesser alternative apparently *do not* choose it, not proportionately as well as they do others. This can be seen by comparing the first two columns of each example in Table 7. There is no reason these two should not be independent (unlike the third column, which depends on the first two), but they are not. The two disadvantages are correlated sharply in the way both fall on the same lesser alternatives.

This correlation has unhappy implications socially, for we usually reassure ourselves about the unfairness of mass popularity by believing the contrary. We console ourselves that the obscure alternative is at least appreciated by the people who *do* know it; for example, the out-of-the-way book is at least a delight to those who find it. That this can happen is visible in occasional reversals in the comics data that we know were due to special merit.[16] Otherwise, however, the null or expected result is in the opposite direction, with the two disadvantages doubling up unhappily in the same places.

One explanation might be that the lesser alternative is lesser known *because* it lacks merit. This lack then shows up as a lack of "liking" as well. True, but our model suggests a simpler and more general explanation that requires no assumption about merit and, indeed, has unfortunate social implications for just that reason of independence of merit. The explanation is that the lesser-known alternative is known to people who know too many *competitive* alternatives. It is being judged by people who have a lot to choose from, whereas the favored or "obvious" alternative is

16. Interestingly, the three comic strips that were liked better than "par" for their renown in 1947 were new ones, for example, Mary Worth, that subsequently *improved* in renown (readership) in a 1949 study. Comics that were better known than liked were prewar ones, for example, Moon Mullins, that have probably declined in readership since.

the one that becomes known to the kind of people who, in making choices, know little *else* to choose from.

This explanation becomes clear, virtually tautological, in the comic-strip example. In that case it was known from other analyses that the people who read only two or three comics tended disproportionately to read "Blondie," "Dick Tracy," and the like. (Indeed, such readers are what give "Blondie" and "Dick Tracy" their relative popularity over comics read by comics fans only.) When, however, the former people who read (know) only two or three are asked to choose the "best three," then what else could they choose? That is, suppose that for any alternative i the probability of its choice among those who know it, as one of k known in total, is

$$P\ (C_i;P_i)\ =\ \frac{c}{k} \tag{25}$$

where c is some number to be chosen, say, 3, as in the case of the "three best" comics. Then for people who know only $k = 3$ comics in all, of which one is "Blondie," the probability of including "Blondie" among their "best three" final choices is 1.

Many real-life applications have exactly this restriction. For example, we can choose only one restaurant to eat at, $c = 1$. If we are uninformed about restaurants and know, for instance, only the two most obviously popular ones in the area, then $k = 2$, and these popular or "obvious" alternatives have probabilities of $\frac{1}{2}$ of being chosen. On the other hand, now consider the problem of the *unobvious* alternatives, for example, a dozen other smaller restaurants we did not know about. The man who knows, say, 10 restaurants in the area is the one who knows these unobvious ones; but choosing from 10, he gives each he knows an average of only $\frac{1}{10}$ chance of being chosen. The unobvious alternatives, then, are known to the kind of people who, knowing many, make the conditional probability of choosing any one, $P\ (C_i;P_i) = c/k$, small for each because k is large.

In situations where the choice is simply "liking" alternatives, however, there is no restriction that everyone choose the same number, c. In other words, there would be no automatic disadvantage for the lesser alternatives because the competitors known with them are numerous. For, the people knowing so many might also like more or choose more of them; that is, c might be large where k is large. In that event, it would be some defect other than the ratio c/k—for example, genuine lack of merit—that gives less publicized alternatives their lesser probability of being liked when known. This conclusion surely is so in some cases, but the general result in our data is to the contrary.

In Table 8 the data on "liking" our radio announcers are tabulated with the number of *competitors* known to the people involved, that is, $k - 1$, held constant. The samples get tiny, and accordingly the alternatives have to be grouped; but the special attraction of the top alternatives compared with the lesser alternatives, in choices of the "like" variety, disappears when the total

Table 8

Liking of Alternatives Known When the Total Known Is Held Constant

$P\ (C_i; P_i)$ = Proportion Who Like an Alternative among Those Who Know It; All Instances for:

Among People Who Know in Total $k =$	Brinkley Gallop Downs	Others	(N = instances)[a]
One (only this one)	.56	.54	(27) (13)
Two	.35	.31	(57) (35)
Three	.26	.30	(68) (46)
Four	.38	.20	(56) (49)
Five	.36	.30	(25) (30)
Six	.35	.54	(14) (22)
Seven	.08	.13	(12) (16)
Eight (all of them)	(.52)[b]	(.24)[b]	(21) (35)

a. Number of people is much smaller than instances, for example, for number of people divide by k. Data were missing in several cases.

b. About half of the 7 persons involved are plainly the "all sayers" and related interviewer failures discussed in footnote 17.

number of alternatives the person is judging from is held equal.[17] If anything, our middle alternatives fare slightly better than the top ones; but in the main, the probability of "liking" (in these data, especially or enthusiastically) varies systematically, not with the particular alternative, but with the number of competitors *relative* to which it is being judged.

Therefore, with larger samples, some version of

$$P\ (C_i;P_i)\ =\ \frac{c}{k} \qquad (25)$$

would probably turn out to be good theory for many "liking" data as well as the other cases where it (tautologically) is the expected, for example, the comics and restaurants examples and in most legal voting (wherever c cannot vary with k). Recalling that the final choice or "like" vote as a proportion of the whole population is $P(C_i) = P_i\,P(C_i;P_i)$, we can substitute to get

$$P\ (C_i\ )\ =\ \sum_{k=1}^{n} P\ (k \text{ and } i)\,\frac{c}{k} \qquad (26)$$

as the proportion of final choices expected in observed data. By coincidence it has the same logical form (except for the constant c)

17. The test is to solve $P\ (C_i;P_i)\ =\ c/k$ for c. It averages $c\ =\ 1.15$ for the top three alternatives in Table 8, $c\ =\ 1.22$ for the others, if we exclude the great weight otherwise of the suspect data in $k\ =\ 8$ discussed below. (With the additional seven cases involved, the averages jump to $c\ =\ 1.52$ for the top three and $c\ =\ 1.30$ for the others.) The coefficient c is *not* a constant in these data; rather, it is larger in the middle ranges of 3 to 6 known. But, except for the crucial point that the advantages of the top alternatives disappear when k is held constant, we do not develop this "choice" part of the theory here.

Some technical evidence in Table 8 bearing on the dubiousness of the $m_3\ =\ 65$ estimates earlier is that about half of the people who claimed they "knew all (eight) of them" now say they "like them all" or "all but . . . ." Interviewer failures that accept such global answers without detail should be excluded in serious applications because of the great moment such answers can have in solutions; for example, our m_3 case is a good (horrible) example.

as did the *relative renown* of the alternatives, the share the alternative had of all instances of knowing alternatives. Recall that renown was biased in favor of popular alternatives to the degree that these alternatives got the unique increments from people who did not know many other competitors as well. Perhaps it is not coincidence that there is an analog in the expression here for the final choices, because the same mechanism is at work—the greater competition present whenever lesser alternatives occur.

Yet here it is really a doubling of the disadvantages of the lesser alternative in *two* distinct processes. The lesser alternative is first of all in jeopardy in the numerator of (26) above. P (k and i) is very small for it when k is small, meaning few ordinary people of moderate knowledge ever come to know of the alternative in the first place. The second jeopardy, cruel in the way it came on top of the first, is that when we finally get to people who *do* know the lesser alternative, that is, when P (k and i) in the numerator does become significant, it is precisely then that the denominator (k) becomes large. (Indeed, it is as if *because* many things are known, this alternative is known). Formally, in expression (26) k becomes a large whole number by which a small probability much smaller than 1 is divided. This larger k means the competition for final choices that we call the "knowledgeability" or "sophistication" in the mind of a person who knows so many alternatives he knows the obscure ones. Unless the unpublicized alternative has special merit, its double jeopardy is (1) not being known and then, (2) when it finally becomes so, being known to people "who know better."

d. *Natural Distributions*

Finally, let us turn to certain "natural" distributions found in popularity data, for example, a J-shaped distribution found by G. Zipf and others to be puzzlingly common in data that have the same logical form—rank by frequencies of human choice or action

—as our popularity problem.[18] This is discussed below, but the present theory bears more closely on another distribution that, although not so widely publicized, shows promise, in work by J. Coleman and others, of being equally common in social affairs. And it is as puzzling as the J-shaped case was earlier why such a precise mathematical form should be "natural" in human data. It is an exponential distribution in the *ratios* between choices of successive alternatives down a ranking of such alternatives by the number of such choices (by popularity). Each tends to be a constant fraction of the previous one.

Let $P(C_i)$ be the proportion choosing the ith alternative when the labeling is now that i is the ith-ranking alternative in a popularity order, $1, 2, \ldots, i, i+1, \ldots, n$, by $P(C)$, that is, by the numbers of final choices of each. And let $P(C_{i+1})$ be the proportion choosing the next-ranked alternative. Then the relationship tends toward,

$$\frac{P(C_{i+1})}{P(C_i)} \approx \text{constant} \qquad (i = 1, 2, 3, \ldots, n)$$

That choices of each are a constant fraction of choices of the next is a sort of null tendency that emerges in averages: extreme ranks like 1 and 2 are subject to much variability. (And data on *un*popular alternatives below the most successful n of them—for example, below the "top ten" or "best" sellers—are seldom reported and thus less certain.)

This result favors the *top* alternatives, for the frequencies of choice of successively less popular alternatives fall off, not linearly, but rapidly at first. For, the falloff is a constant fraction of the next higher alternative, and thus the relative advantages

18. The regularity in question is not a relation between the frequency of choices, as in our case, but in the number of *alternatives* that receive a fixed number of choices or more than a certain number. See H. A. Simon, "On a Class of Skew Distribution Functions," in *Models for Man* (New York: Wiley, 1957). This paper gives numerous references, and the mathematical reader will find the distribution as the limit of Yule's birth and death model of biological species.

(differences) are largest at the top. Or, going up, the higher one goes, the greater the increments at each step.

All three examples of the final choices in Table 7, earlier, tended to this form; the reader can see the sharp rise of top choices by reranking each P (C_i) column. Coleman finds it in the averages of data for best-selling books, top hit tunes, and sociometric choices.[19] Stephan and Mischler find it in data on frequency of participation in small groups, a form of popularity in the flow of remarks.[20]

Figure 3 shows why the present model tends toward this same result. On the left are shown alternatives ranked by P_i, or the proportion who know of them. We illustrate these proportions linearly related, that is, *not* themselves exponential. In the next diagram to the right, the *same* ranking of the alternatives is preserved, but now what is plotted is P $(C_i;P_i)$, or the probability of liking or choosing the alternative if one knows it. We show these conditional choices correlated with P_i, or renown, this being the "double-jeopardy" result whereby the lesser known are less chosen by those who know them, as the general expectation.

Now, since the final or observed choice is

$$P \ (C_i) \ = \ P_i \ P(C_i;P_i)$$

the first two sets of frequencies are *multiplied* to produce the kind of final choices that are reported as sales of best-sellers and the like. As plotted on the right, this product yields a nonlinear distribution of final choices favoring the top alternatives. For example, $.8 \times .8 = .64$ gives more than three-fourths of the original, but $.5 \times .5 = .25$ gives only $\frac{1}{2}$, and $.3 \times .3 = .09$ only about a third of the original. In other words, one is reducing things that are already smaller, more than proportionately down still more.

19. In drafts of *Mathematics and Sociology* (New York: The Free Press of Glencoe, forthcoming).

20. In P. Hare, E. F. Borgatta, and R. F. Bales, eds., *Small Groups* (New York: Alfred A. Knopf, 1955).

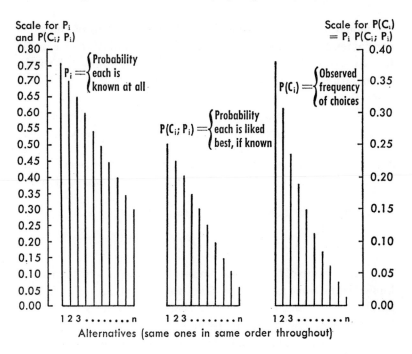

Figure 3

Choices as nonlinear product of linear orders in renown and liking.

Thus, the distribution of final choices, the only observed data usually, is concave, "scooped out." Qualitatively, then, linearlike differences in public renown would in any such two-step process yield, exponentiallike differences in final choice.

If the qualitative tendency toward concavity follows from the model, what is puzzling is this: Why should the empirical distributions—like the rankings of sales of top hit tunes over many weeks—average out so closely, as Coleman finds, to *precise* exponential form? We cannot prove that this model would always produce the same, but it can be shown why it would tend to that result in similar averaging. The argument displays properties of the model of interest beyond the empirical problem of the exponential tendency in popularity. But the nontechnical reader would be advised perhaps to skip the following "Discussion" to the "Conclusions" that follow it *on page 149.*

DISCUSSION. First, let us give a name to the number of alternatives a person knows *other* than alternative i, namely, r, where

$r + 1 = k$ when i is known (that is, total = others plus i)
$\quad r = k$ when i is not known (that is, total = others alone)

From the first definition it follows that

$$P \ (r \text{ and } i) = P \ (k \text{ and } i) \tag{27}$$

since, for example, four others known excluding i and then i also known is the same as $4 + 1 = 5$ known in total, including i. Next let $P \ (r \text{ and } \bar{i})$ be the probability that r others are known and i is *not* known. Then form the ratio, $P \ (r \text{ and } i)/P(r \text{ and } \bar{i})$, or the relative occurrence of i versus not-i when the others are held constant. This ratio within one M group alone gives a taste not only of the gruesome-looking combinatorial expressions that can occur in this model but of the hopeful prospects for simplifying them:

$$\frac{P \ (r \text{ and } i)}{P \ (r \text{ and } \bar{i})} =$$

$$\sum_{x=0}^{\infty} e^{-m} \frac{m^x}{x!} \left\{ \frac{(1 - q_i{}^x) \sum_{j \neq i} \left[\prod_r (1 - q_j{}^x) \prod_{n-r} q_j{}^x \right]}{q_i{}^x \sum_{j \neq i} \left[\prod_r (1 - q_j{}^x) \prod_{n-r} q_j{}^x \right]} \right\} \tag{28}$$

where on the right Π_r means the product of r terms like the one following it and here $\Sigma_{j \neq i}$ means the sum over all the combinations of alternatives other than i that could occur in the r and $n - r$ arrangements following. All these products on the right in brackets cancel out, and the remaining terms in m and q_i alone can be shown to sum to[21]

$$\frac{P \ (r \text{ and } i)}{P \ (r \text{ and } \bar{\imath})} = e^{mp_i/q_i} - 1 \tag{29}$$

We neglect here that there are three M groups each with different m's, with the weight shifting between them with increasing r, so that the simplicity of expression (29) is *not* apparent in observed data.[22]

Next, the result in expression (29) just above can be shown, with algebraic rearrangement and letting

$$P \ (r \text{ and } i) + P \ (r \text{ and } \bar{\imath}) = P \ (R = r),$$

to be[23]

$$(1 - e^{-mp_i/q_i}) \ P \ (R = r) = P \ (r \text{ and } i)$$
$$= P \ (k \text{ and } i) \tag{30}$$

---

21. The right side of (28) becomes

$$\sum_x e^{-m} \left[\frac{(m/q)^x}{x!} - \frac{m^x}{x!} \right]$$

which are e^x series inside the brackets when summed over x. Therefore,

$$e^{-m}(e^{m/q} - e^m) = e^{-m(1-1/q)} - 1$$

Then the exponent can be rewritten

$$-m \left(\frac{q-1}{q} \right) = +m \frac{p}{q}$$

to give the result (29).

22. When we subtract calculated data for group M_1 out of the real data and then examine the residuals, they do conform to (29) within the variability of small N. And they should have been taken more seriously, since, when solved for m_2, it came out about 11, rather than the 12 we used, which the earlier Figure 1 shows was a little too high.

23. Add 1 to both sides in (29), and then rewrite it as

$$\frac{P \ (r \text{ and } i) + P \ (r \text{ and } \bar{\imath})}{P \ (r \text{ and } i)} = e^{mp/q}$$

As the text said, we let the numerator be $P \ (R = r)$. Then inverting, we have

$$\frac{P \ (r \text{ and } \bar{\imath})}{P \ (R = r)} = e^{-mp/q}$$

the last being true by the definitions leading to expression (27) previously. Next, recalling earlier results in (26) that the final or observed choices were expected to be

$$P\ (C_i) = \sum_{k=1}^{n} P\ (k \text{ and } i)\ \frac{c}{k} \tag{26}$$

we may substitute the left side of expression (30) for $P\ (k \text{ and } i)$ here. With rearranging and new labeling, it becomes

$$P\ (C_i) = (1 - e^{-mp_i/q_i}) \sum_{r=0}^{n-1} P\ (R = r)\ \frac{c}{r+1} \tag{31}$$

the substitution of $r + 1$ for k being permissible because by expression (30) we have defined the cases $P\ (r \text{ and } i)$, where i is known in addition to the r.

Now, in a ratio of two such expressions for alternatives of adjacent rank in popularity, $P\ (C_{i+1})/P(C_i)$, all terms to the right summed over r in (31) cancel out for practical purposes, leaving

$$\frac{P\ (C_{i+1})}{P\ (C_i)} \approx \frac{1 - e^{-mp_{i+1}/q_{i+1}}}{1 - e^{-mp_i/q_i}} \tag{32}$$

This is because the other terms for each adjacent alternative differed only in that the definition of r in $R = r$ in one case includes $i + 1$ but excludes i and in the other includes i but excludes $i + 1$. For sizable n this substitution of *adjacent* alternatives for one another is of negligible import.

But $P\ (r \text{ and } \bar{\imath}) = P\ (R = r) - P\ (r \text{ and } i)$. Substituting this value, we obtain

$$\frac{P\ (R = r)}{P\ (R = r)} - \frac{P\ (r \text{ and } i)}{P\ (R = r)} = e^{-mp/q}$$

$$1 - e^{-mp/q} = \frac{P\ (r \text{ and } i)}{P\ (R = r)}$$

and multiplying through by $P\ (R = r)$ gives expression (30) of the text.

Next, let

$$\frac{p_{i+1}}{q_{i+1}} = \frac{p_i}{q_i} - d(i+1)$$
$$\frac{p_{i-1}}{q_{i-1}} = \frac{p_i}{q_i} + d(i-1)$$

(33)

where $d(\ )$ is just a name for the difference in each case, whatever it is. Indeed, we want to find out *what* these differences would have to be, if

$$\frac{P(C_{i+1})}{P(C_i)} \approx \frac{P(C_i)}{P(C_{i-1})}$$

the exponential case. Forming this expression in the manner of (32) and substituting (33), we get, as what would be necessary for exponential ordering,

$$\frac{1 - \exp\left[-m\frac{p_i}{q_i} + md(i+1)\right]}{1 - \exp\left(-m\frac{p_i}{q_i}\right)}$$
$$\approx \frac{1 - \exp\left(-m\frac{p_i}{q_i}\right)}{1 - \exp\left[-m\frac{p_i}{q_i} - md(i-1)\right]}$$

(34)

where $\exp[\ ]$ is understood to mean the exponent of e. Cross-multiplying, dividing through by $\exp[-m(p_i/q_i)]$, and collecting terms, we reach the condition that

$$2 - e^{md(i+1)} - e^{-md(i-1)} \approx e^{-mp_i/q_i}[1 - e^{md(i+1)-md(i-1)}] \quad (35)$$

must be approximately satisfied for data from such a model to be indistinguishable from the exponential ordering.

The general region of conditions that satisfy this approximation very closely is when the parameters of these alternatives (that have achieved adjacent positions on a list of successful ones, for example, nearly identical success on the best-seller lists) are separated by *small linear* differences. Or these differences may be "less than linear," in the sense that top alternatives can be, if anything, separated by even smaller differences than the differences between lesser alternatives in p values; and yet the exponential consequences whereby they have much greater dominance in choices nevertheless appear. As an example of the latter, let

$$d(i + 1) = d(i - 1) = d = \text{constant for all } i \qquad (36)$$

or

$$\frac{p_{i+1}}{q_{i+1}} + d = \frac{p_i}{q_i} = \frac{p_{i-1}}{q_{i-1}} - d$$

which is giving top alternatives *less* increment in p over their neighbors than the lower alternatives over theirs, since linear increments in p would increase p/q more than this among the top alternatives (where q is significantly different from 1). Substituting in expression (35), we obtain

$$2 - e^{+md} - e^{-md} \approx e^{-mp_i/q_i}(1 - e^{+md-md}) \approx 0 \qquad (37)$$

and dividing by $2e^m$, we get as condition (35) for exponential consequences

$$\frac{e^{-m(1-d)} + e^{-m(1+d)}}{2} \approx e^{-m} \qquad (38)$$

Because e^{-m} is not sensitive to small differences in the exponent (as is e^m), this would be closely approximated by only very *loose* resemblances to the equalities set up in expression (36) before.

Now consider strictly linear differences[24] in p; that is

$$\frac{p_i - d}{q_i + d} = \frac{p_{i+1}}{q_{i+1}} \qquad (d = \text{constant for all } i) \qquad (39)$$

(which is confusing because rank $i + 1$ is *lower* than i, hence, $p - d$). Substituting (39) in (35) yields a like version of (35) to

---

24. Linear differences in p mean that in (33) and (35)

$$d(i + 1) = \left[\frac{p_i}{q_i} - \frac{p_i - d}{q_i + d} \right] = \frac{d}{q_i^2 + q_i d} \quad \text{and} \quad d(i - 1) = \frac{d}{q_i^2 - q_i d}$$

without signs that are already embodied in expression (35), in which we satisfy for exponential ordering in choices:

$$\frac{e^{-m/(q+d)} + e^{-m/(q-d)}}{2} \approx e^{-m/q} \tag{40}$$

which, as inspection of an e^{-x} table will show, is a weak condition that is tolerant of substantial deviations from strict equality (linearity) of the small d's involved.

Both conditions, expressions (38) and (40), are "loose" then, easily approximated in a degree that would be indistinguishable from the exponential form in empirical data. Or more to the point, it would take special cases to *escape* the tendency, and these are just what the averaging of empirical results eliminates.

CONCLUSIONS. So, the exponentiallike order in the final choices—a dominance structure favoring those near to the top in the proportion they *are* at the top, or in growth in rank giving an increasingly large increment in choices with each increase in rank—is fostered merely by any small *linear*like, indeed, by less strong than linear differences in the parameters p. The two chief implications are these: one descriptive and one normative.

1. Most distributions from which parameters would be samples, like the normal and Poisson, become linearlike beyond the

---

wish to substitute. Making that substitution, we obtain

$$2 - \exp\left[m\left(\frac{d}{q^2 + qd}\right)\right] - \exp\left[-m\left(\frac{d}{q^2 - qd}\right)\right]$$

$$\approx \left[\exp\left(-m\frac{p}{q}\right)\right]\left[1 - \exp\left(\frac{md}{q^2 + qd} - \frac{md}{q^2 - qd}\right)\right]$$

where the subscript of q and p is always i. The exponent on the far right expands to $-2m[d^2/(q^3 - qd^2)]$. If we remain within the region the text discusses, *small* differences between adjacent parameters, the numerator d^2 will be virtually zero. (Its typical value is .000+ for our radio data.) This means the right side of the equation is

$$\frac{1 - e^{-.0+}}{e^{mp/q}} \approx 0$$

Dividing the remaining (left) side of the equation by $2e^{mp/q}$, we simplify to obtain (40) in the text.

mean in what is called the "tail" of the distribution, but here the "head," for the *successful* alternatives that make the best-seller lists, "top tens," and the like are representative of parameters well above the mean. Small, linearlike differences of parameters would be hard to escape in any sampling, and then averaging for identical ranks, among "pre-eminent" alternatives. The resulting exponential distribution of choices—not just in this model but in Coleman's empirical findings—may be as "natural" in the consequences as a normal distribution of the causes.[25]

2. Speaking normatively or manipulatively, the parameter p is like publicity and q like keeping quiet. Under conditions appropriate to this model (chiefly that people know only a fraction of the alternatives, as in choosing books or other people), the suggestion is hard to escape that *linear* increments of publicity and advertising, or renown, bring *exponential* increments in choices, or popularity.

Indeed, returns could be greater. Let us see a connection between this exponential regularity in popularity data and the J-shaped distributions found (for example, by Zipf) in the number of cities of a certain population size, the number of words used with a certain frequency, and so on. The latter are also popularity data, in a sense, but with this difference: the alternatives in those cases are relatively *permanent*, not just this month's "top tunes," but cities, words, and the like. Thus, each's popu-

---

25. Two actual experiments have been tried with parameters for this model normally distributed in the following sense. Ten points equally spaced by area (that is, distances between them equally probable) under half the normal curve have been taken as what the typical positions of parameters in some "top ten" would be. Then making p_i proportionate to the standard deviation of each, for example, its "merit" or publicity better than the mean, choices were generated in an earlier version of this model that were exponential with error only in the third decimal place. With the present model, the same array of parameters makes the right side of (32), and thus $P(C_i)/P(C_{i+1})$ such that it be indistinguishable from constant in empirical data, except at the extremes very near the mean and near three or more standard deviations away. We have *not* examined, however, what the presence of three different M groups in the present model would do to all this.

larity today can affect its future popularity, for example, the more people who settle in San Francisco, the greater its future growth.

To show why the permanency is important, suppose we retain the same alternatives in the present model for a new cycle, for example, another Monte Carlo run representing next year or next decade. But now in setting p_i for the next cycle, let

$$p_i = f \, P(C_i) \tag{41}$$

where f is, say, some proportionality constant and it is understood that p_i is now for time $t + 1$. Then there will be "feedback" from *choices* this time to the parameter affecting *renown* next time. If we then let this continue for many cycles, with renown growing on choice and choice on renown (and if we also assume that with the passage of time new alternatives enter and extend the list), then the conditions are met that H. A. Simon sets down for the J-shaped distribution to appear as the limit.[26] So, this model would apparently produce that result as well.

That one model may produce both regularities suggests the connection between these exponentiallike and J-shaped regularities in popularity data—the two "natural" distributions therein. It seems to be a question of transiency versus *permanency* in the alternatives. The latter encourages feedback from choices to renown, or growth that feeds on itself, and that produces a more top-heavy dominance structure that, looked at in a different way, is like the J phenomenon.

Brief explorations of a computer version of this model with the above feedback arrangements suggest it does not remedy the discouraging facts of this paper.[27] The picture is, instead, worse.

26. Benoit Mandelbrot, on mathematical grounds that the technical reader can find in *Information and Control*, September, 1961, disputes that such conditions actually generate the precise form of the J-curve as it appears in, say, word frequencies.
27. I am indebted to Emmy Lou Miller—then of Watson Laboratory of Columbia University, to which thanks also go—for exploring this problem. Results are a pronounced J-like distribution in which the first several alter-

The feedback model apparently leads to still more overweighting of the marginal person, more monopoly of the few popular alternatives over the uninformed people, not just double but repetitive jeopardies for the less renowned alternative, and now more than exponentiallike returns from sustained publicity.

Popularity is a happy topic, evidently, only for the popular.

Technical Note

Perhaps no greater annual investment is made in social research than measuring mass exposure to information. Anything that can be done to make efficient measurement instruments out of models in this domain, then, is guaranteed to be used.

Accordingly, data in the detailed form needed for sophisticated measurement work are tabulated in Table 9 below. Where

---

natives come into marked dominance, while choices of the other ranks become a flat "tail" asymptotic to zero. (As explained in Note 18, however, this must be examined in a different way to show its connection with what is called the J-curve in the text.)

algebraic progress on the problem now stands is reported below under (1) solutions for parameters and (2) calculating problems.

1. PARAMETERS

It is easy to get solutions for this model with extreme simplifying assumptions such as

$$\sum_{i=1}^{n} p_i = 1$$

(or that some outcome happens on every trial). It is thanks not just to criticism of this kind of assumption by Albert Madansky, but to his practical demonstration that a more general method is feasible, that the initial results to follow were found. We use a perhaps more intuitive route than his, but the end result is the same.

Let the items that are called the "alternatives" in this paper be numbered in *any* order (as the general case, although practical reasons are given below for using the observed order of popularity). Then let $Q_{1,2,\ldots,h}$ be the observed proportion of people who do *not* know any of the subset of items that were labeled from 1 to h. We take h large enough to be confident that in

$$Q_{1,2,\ldots,h} = M_1 \sum_{x=0}^{\infty} e^{-m_1} \frac{m_1^x}{x!} (q_1^x q_2^x \cdots q_h^x) + \cdots \quad (42)$$

we can neglect the terms omitted on the right for the contributions of groups other than the M_1 shown. That is, as explained earlier in the text, when the population is stratified, M_1, $M_2, \ldots$, in order upward from those least exposed, we can define some state of nonknowledge, $Q_{1,2,\ldots,h}$, that would be very unlikely to occur in any but the *least* exposed stratum of people, M_1. The practical way to ensure this is to include "obvious" items of information, and let these be the ones numbered 1,

2, . . . , h, where none but the virtually unexposed people could plausibly remain ignorant of *all h* of them.

The sum on the right of (42) is the expected proportion of people who will fail to learn any of these alternatives. This expands, of course, as follows:

$$M_1 \left\{ e^{-m} + e^{-m} \left[mq_1q_2 \cdot \cdot \cdot q_h + \frac{(mq_1q_2 \cdot \cdot \cdot q_h)^2}{2!} + \cdot \cdot \cdot \right. \right.$$
$$\left. \left. + \frac{(m_1q_2 \cdot \cdot \cdot q_h)^x}{x!} + \cdot \cdot \cdot \right] \right\}$$
$$= M_1[e^{-m} + e^{-m}(e^{mq_1q_2 \cdots q_h} - 1)]$$
$$= M_1 e^{-m(1 - q_1q_2 \cdots q_h)}$$

(since the sum in the braces above was an e^x series, minus its first term, 1). This result is, by (42), equal to the observed quantity, $Q_{1,2\ldots h}$. Substituting, we can rewrite (42) in natural logarithms

$$\log Q_{1,2\ldots h} = \log M_1 - m_1(1 - q_1q_2 \cdot \cdot \cdot q_h) \qquad (43)$$

$$m_1q_1q_2 \cdot \cdot \cdot q_h = \log Q_{1,2\ldots h} - \log M_1 + m_1 \qquad (44)$$

Let us juxtapose to this equation an analogous expression:

$$m_1q_1q_2 \cdot \cdot \cdot q_hq_i = \log Q_{1,2,\ldots,h,i} - \log M_1 + m_1 \qquad (45)$$

which is the equivalent of (44) for the nonknowledge of the same alternatives *and* of alternative i as well. Now subtract expression (45) from (44) to eliminate M_1 and m_1 on the right. We now have

$$m_1q_1q_2 \cdot \cdot \cdot q_h(1 - q_i) = \log Q_{1,2,\ldots,h} - \log Q_{1,2,\ldots,h,i} \qquad (46)$$

Next, proceed to define analogous observed quantities $Q_{1,2,\ldots,h,j}$ and $Q_{1,2,\ldots,h,i,j}$. These are, as above, the proportions of people who do not know the h items and the h items plus i, respectively, *and* who also do not know j. Subtract from one another logarithmic expressions for these quantities analogous to (44) and (45). The result is an expression identical to (46) except for the presence of j in all terms. Dividing it by (46), we obtain a solution for q_j:

$$\frac{m_1 q_1 q_2 \cdots q_h (1 - q_i) q_j}{m_1 q_1 q_2 \cdots q_h (1 - q_i)} = q_j$$
$$= \frac{\log Q_{1,2,\ldots,h,j} - \log Q_{1,2,\ldots,h,i,j}}{\log Q_{1,2,\ldots,h} - \log Q_{1,2,\ldots,h,i}} \quad (47)$$

Since the theory is not meaningful without a sizable n—more alternatives than everyone could easily know—the model is over-determined and a number of different solutions like this for any q_j are obtainable. Here is where the unfinished business in mathematical statistics begins, for example, the need for maximum likelihood estimates

Meanwhile, for what it is worth to practitioners who want to go ahead with existing procedures, our experience in this one case is that the following gives quite stable estimates of the general magnitudes of the p's and q's, for example, Σp varying less than .03. The stable Σp is all that is necessary to find M_1 and the like (after which minor irregularities in individual p and q estimates can be corrected by means below).

First, as is obvious to the technical reader, one should *not* try to average separate solutions to (47). Rather, prior to the division there, the averaging procedure that is defensible logically and leads to stable results in practice is to add expressions in the form of (46) and its analog in the numerator of (47), and only then do the division in (47) with the sums. Putting this formally, let $s(h)$ be any set of h of the items that are appropriate to the simplifying assumptions in expression (42), and let item j be any item not appropriate and thus *not* included in $s(h)$. In practice, $s(h)$ should be combinations of the most popular items; we used Brinkley, Downs, Gallop, and Blair with the size of $h = 3$ to give four sets of $s(h)$. And let i be any (and every) item not in h, except j. Then the algebra of (47) remains true of the sums over all sets of h

each used in combination with every item i:

$$\frac{m_1 q_j \sum\limits_{s(h)} \sum\limits_{i \neq j} \prod\limits_h q(1 - q_i)}{m_1 \sum\limits_{s(h)} \sum\limits_{i \neq j} \prod\limits_h q(1 - q_i)} = q_j \qquad (48)$$

where Πq is the product of the h number of q's in each set, $\Sigma_{s(h)}$ is the sum over all such sets, and $\Sigma_{i \neq j}$ is the sum for each set over all items available to use as i. Thus, an estimate of q_j using a very *large* amount of information is the sums of all the observables corresponding to the ratio in (48), namely, sums comparably analogous now to the right side of (47):

$$q_j = \frac{\sum\limits_{s(h)} \sum\limits_{i \neq j} (\log Q \ldots_{h,j} - \log Q \ldots_{h,i,j})}{\sum\limits_{s(h)} \sum\limits_{i \neq j} (\log Q \ldots_h - \log Q \ldots_{h,i})} \qquad (49)$$

In this manner, one determines $q_{h+1}, q_{h+2}, \ldots, q_n$. Next, q_1, $q_2, \ldots, q_h$ can be found by substitution of the known q's in expressions involving them and combinations of these unknown $q_1, q_2 \ldots, q_h$. Or one can form sums of observables corresponding to, say,

$$q_1 = \frac{m_1 q_1 \sum\limits_s \prod\limits_s q}{m_1 \sum\limits_s \prod\limits_s q} \qquad (50)$$

where s is any large set of items, for example, 2, 3, $\ldots$, h, $h + 1, \ldots$, which is deemed equivalent to earlier combinations involving item 1, in that none but the lightly exposed M_1 would be ignorant of all of the set s—the spirit of simplifying assumption (42) earlier.

Just as the average magnitudes of p's and q's seem fairly stable in different ways of forming these large sums, as said earlier, the same now proves true of estimates of m_1. For m_1 is estimated from the same large amount of summed information. Consider all of the sums that would already have been made in estimating the q's, having the form of sums of (44) and (45). For example, a sum of expressions of the form (44) would be

$$m_1 \sum_{s(h)} \prod_h q = \sum_{s(h)} (\log Q_{1,2,\ldots,h} - \log M_1 + m_1) \qquad (44a)$$

or the sums of expressions like (44) over all sets of h items-each available. One can subtract any two such sums—say, subtract the sum of half of the individual results of the form (44) from the sum of the other half. This process eliminates the log M_1 and m_1 terms on the right, but then all factors are known except m_1 on the left. Therefore, m_1 is determined for an average of as much information as is available. While we showed no decimal points for the m estimates in the text, that was to convey that $m_2 = 12$ varied at least ± 1 and that m_3 was suspect, but *not* that estimates of m_1 were unstable. (Our various estimates were all within .1 of 4.0.)

Given m_1 and the p's and then substituting them in sums like (44a), we can determine the remaining unknown there, M_1, for the very large amount of information so summed. Our estimates of M_1 were somewhat less stable, however, varying between .7 and .8, closer to .8. We used .7 from other considerations not now believed so cogent.

Given m_1 and M_1, one can proceed by methods that amount to fitting the residuals unaccounted for by them alone and thus forcing one to postulate additional M groups. One method proceeds by first reducing the set of h items used as "stratifiers" above to a smaller set of size $h - 1$. And correspondingly, reduce the "order" of $Q_{1,2,\ldots}$ to one item less, that is, define a new combination of not knowing items $Q_{1,2,\ldots,h-1}$. Then test the fit of the corresponding version of (42) analogously simplified to

$$Q_{1,2,\ldots,h-1} \overset{?}{=} M_1 \exp\left[-m_1(1 - q_1 q_2 \cdots q_{h-1})\right] \qquad (51)$$

where we express by $\overset{?}{=}$ that this may still be very close to equality, since on the average it was exactly satisfied for the set of size *h.* (We assume comparable averaging here.) If the residual error in (51) is still small, as is likely, reduce to $h - 2$ and continue to test for significant residuals. If only one M group will be sufficient to fit the data, this test will find no systematic residuals of error down to $Q_i = M_1 e^{-m_1 q_i}$.

In our data, however, significant residual soon began to show up. When these are large enough to work with stably, one has then identified the presence of a second (or more) M group. Assume this group occurs with a set of size g, where $h > g$, of course. That is, we cannot fit $Q_{1,2,\ldots,g}$-type data with (51). Then assume analogous to (42) and (43) earlier that

$$Q_{1,2,\ldots,g} = M_1 \exp\left[-m_1(1 - q_1 q_2 \cdots q_g)\right]$$
$$+ M_2 \exp\left[-m_2(1 - q_1 q_2 \cdots q_g)\right] + \cdots$$

where the upper group of terms on the right is now known. Therefore, shifting them to the left side and passing to logs, we obtain

$$\log\{Q_{1,2,\ldots,g} - M_1 \exp\left[-m_1(1 - q_1 q_2 \cdots q_g)\right]\}$$
$$\approx \log M_2 + m_2(1 - q_1 q_2 \cdots q_g) \quad (52)$$

This relation would be exactly satisfied if there were only one more M group, M_2 (but also satisfied if the further M_3, M_4, . . . groups had such high densities of exposure that they were not involved in any Q or "nonknowledge," the case in our data). To put it another way, (52) postulates the minimum, or "simplest," structure, only one additional M group, M_2, which we accept until subsequent failures to fit may force the identification of still further groups. Since all quantities in (52) are known except M_2 and m_2, we are now in the same position as at expression (44a) with the first group, and the solution for M_2 and m_2 proceeds analogously.

Given M_1 and M_2 and m_1 and m_2, further tests analogous to (51) may not now identify a third group reliably (for the reason in parentheses in the paragraph above). The necessity to postulate still further M groups, or strata, if any, would make itself apparent only in calculations or Monte Carlo results like those shown in Figure 1 of the main text. For example, P $(K = k)$ would begin falling systematically short beyond some k, in our case P $(K = 7)$. Then other formulas not dependent on the zero term, $Q_{1,2}...$, which are discussed in the next section, could be used to make estimates from residuals. In our case, we simply postulated the minimum size $M_3 = .05$ necessary to fit the residuals in P (7) and P (8), the "bump" on the tail of the distribution. We then determined $m_3 = 65$ by what was necessary to produce the observed ratio P (8)$/P$ (7) among such people.

It is obviously the case that procedures become less clear (and estimates less stable), as we proceed from M_1 to M_n. Therefore, it would probably be best to settle for a two-class model until better statistical procedures are available, including for continuous distributions by m, the actual case in the real world.

A final point: once the M's and m's are settled upon, then in real applications it will be desirable to iterate, varying each p_i by appropriate small steps up or down, until

$$Q_i = \sum_M Me^{-mp_i} \tag{53}$$

or the marginals for each item are satisfied exactly. The p_i that satisfies this would be taken as the final one, those from the earlier (48) being of the right average magnitude but individually irregular. To satisfy (53) iteratively is not too tedious, but in this respect and others the final estimates in which we happened to invest the Monte Carlo run, and which we thus used for illustration in this paper, were averages, including results from other considerations implied below that we now believe not as cogent as the procedures above.

2. CALCULATING PROBLEMS

Turning now to calculating problems, we find that they are not prohibitive except with very large n; but mathematical simplifications of the following procedures or approximations for

Table 9

Specific Combinations of Alternatives Known

Total known k =	Brinkley	Gallop	Downs	Blair	Brandt	Collins	Russell	Hamilton	No. of cases, N =
8	1	1	1	1	1	1	1	1	7
7	1	1	1	1	1	1	1	0	1
7	1	1	1	1	1	1	0	1	1
7	1	1	1	1	0	1	1	1	1
7	1	1	1	0	1	1	1	1	1
6	1	1	1	1	0	0	1	1	1
6	1	1	1	0	0	1	1	1	1
6	1	1	0	1	1	1	1	0	1
6	1	1	0	1	0	1	1	1	1
6	1	1	0	0	1	1	1	1	1
6	0	1	1	0	1	1	1	1	1
5	1	1	1	1	1	0	0	0	1
5	1	1	1	1	0	0	1	0	1
5	1	1	1	0	0	1	1	0	2
5	1	1	0	1	1	1	0	0	1
5	1	1	0	1	1	0	1	0	1
5	1	1	0	1	0	1	0	1	1
5	1	1	0	0	1	0	1	1	1
5	1	0	1	0	1	1	1	0	1
5	1	0	0	1	0	1	1	1	1
5	0	1	1	1	1	0	1	0	1
4	1	1	1	1	0	0	0	0	2
4	1	1	1	0	1	0	0	0	2
4	1	1	1	0	0	1	0	0	1
4	1	1	1	0	0	0	1	0	1
4	1	1	1	0	0	0	0	1	3
4	1	1	0	1	1	0	0	0	3
4	1	1	0	1	0	1	0	0	1
4	1	1	0	1	0	0	0	1	2
4	1	0	1	1	0	1	0	0	1
4	1	0	1	1	0	0	1	0	2
4	1	0	1	1	0	0	0	1	1
4	1	0	0	1	1	1	0	0	1
4	1	0	0	1	0	1	1	0	1
4	1	0	0	1	0	0	1	1	1

Table 9 (Continued)

Total known k =	Brinkley	Gallop	Downs	Blair	Brandt	Collins	Russell	Hamilton	No. of cases, N =
4	0	1	1	1	0	0	0	1	1
4	0	1	1	0	1	0	0	1	1
4	0	0	1	1	1	0	0	1	1
4	0	0	0	1	1	0	1	1	1
3	1	1	1	0	0	0	0	0	6
3	1	1	0	1	0	0	0	0	1
3	1	1	0	0	1	0	0	0	1
3	1	1	0	0	0	1	0	0	1
3	1	1	0	0	0	0	1	0	1
3	1	1	0	0	0	0	0	1	3
3	1	0	1	1	0	0	0	0	4
3	1	0	1	0	1	0	0	0	3
3	1	0	1	0	0	0	0	1	1
3	1	0	0	1	0	1	0	0	3
3	1	0	0	0	1	0	1	0	1
3	1	0	0	0	1	0	0	1	1
3	0	1	1	0	1	0	0	0	3
3	0	1	0	1	1	0	0	0	2
3	0	1	0	0	0	1	1	0	1
3	0	1	0	0	0	0	1	0	1
3	0	1	0	0	0	0	0	1	1
3	0	0	1	1	1	0	0	0	2
3	0	0	1	0	1	0	1	0	1
3	0	0	1	0	0	1	1	0	1
2	1	1	0	0	0	0	0	0	11
2	1	0	1	0	0	0	0	0	5
2	1	0	0	1	0	0	0	0	5
2	1	0	0	0	1	0	0	0	1
2	1	0	0	0	0	1	0	0	1
2	1	0	0	0	0	0	1	0	1
2	0	1	1	0	0	0	0	0	4
2	0	1	0	1	0	0	0	0	1
2	0	1	0	0	1	0	0	0	3
2	0	1	0	0	0	1	0	0	1
2	0	1	0	0	0	0	1	0	1
2	0	0	1	1	0	0	0	0	1
2	0	0	1	0	1	0	0	0	1
2	0	0	1	0	0	1	0	0	1

Table 9 (Continued)

Total known $k =$	Brinkley	Gallop	Downs	Blair	Brandt	Collins	Russell	Hamilton	No. of cases, $N =$
2	0	0	0	1	1	0	0	0	4
2	0	0	0	1	0	0	0	1	2
2	0	0	0	0	1	1	0	0	1
2	0	0	0	0	0	1	1	0	2
1	1	0	0	0	0	0	0	0	13
1	0	1	0	0	0	0	0	0	8
1	0	0	1	0	0	0	0	0	8
1	0	0	0	1	0	0	0	0	7
1	0	0	0	0	1	0	0	0	2
1	0	0	0	0	0	1	0	0	2
1	0	0	0	0	0	0	1	0	1
1	0	0	0	0	0	0	0	1	1
0	0	0	0	0	0	0	0	0	29

them, would be of great practical value (and seem hopeful). The basic data the theory must reproduce are given in Table 9, and we now proceed to derive an explicit formula for the typical entry therein (or for the probability corresponding to the raw cases there).

Let the set $s(h)$ now be *any* set of h particular items, and $s(n - h)$ be the others. And call the probability that all h will be known and all the $n - h$ not known, $P[h;(n - h)]$. Suitable definitions of h and $n - h$ can thus be made to correspond to any entry in Table 9. The theoretic counterpart of any such table entry is (neglecting for the moment, different M groups)

$$P[h;(n - h)] = \sum_{x=0}^{\infty} e^{-m} \frac{m^x}{x!} \left[\prod_{s(h)} (1 - q^x) \prod_{s(n-h)} q^x \right] \quad (54)$$

where we mean by $\Pi_{s(h)}$ the product of h terms like the one following for the h members of this particular set. To see concretely what (54) means, take $h = 3$ consisting of items i, j, and k as the ones known by respondents, the "yes" items. Then the term in brackets above becomes, after we expand the $h = 3$ terms having the form $1 - q^x$,

$$\left\{[1 - q_i{}^x - q_j{}^x - q_k{}^x + (q_iq_j)^x + (q_iq_k)^x + (q_jq_k)^x \right.$$
$$\left. - (q_iq_jq_k)^x]\prod_{s(n-3)} q^x\right\} \quad (55)$$

and simplifying notation by letting the product of the $n - 3$ q's on the far right be simply π, we can multiply through by π and then by $m^x/x!$ from outside the brackets in the original expression (54). Every resulting product is a typical term in an e^x series, and thus summing over all x as indicated in (54) yields for our example in (55)

$$P[h;(n - h)] = \exp[-m(1 - \pi)] - \exp[-m(1 - q_i\pi)] - \cdots$$
$$\pm \cdots - \exp[-m(1 - q_iq_jq_k\pi)] \quad (58)$$

While there is always a particular sequence of terms and signs, as in expression (55) for our example, it is simply an exercise in notation to generalize these e^x summing operations to any combination $P[h;(n - h)]$. Since the terms in brackets of expressions like (58) are the same for all M groups, except for multiplying by m itself, multiple groups present no difficulty. So expressions of the form (58) generate the theoretic counterpart of the entries in Table 9. From combinations of those entries, in turn, all other results equivalent to the Monte Carlo data in the text can be obtained.

As said in a text note, we were unduly awed by the prospective size of the above calculations; instead we tried to develop the following attractive simplification in which, however, there is some defect that invites competent diagnosis (because, if it can be cleared up, the method would be useful not only in calculations but in solutions). It is best explained as a recursive method, although explicit expressions of a polynomial form seem to be possible. Recall the formula derived in the text:

$$\frac{P \, (r \text{ and } i)}{P \, (r \text{ and } \bar{\imath})} = e^{mp_i/q_i} - 1 \tag{29}$$

$$P \, (r \text{ and } i) = P \, (r \text{ and } \bar{\imath})[e^{mp_i/q_i} - 1] \tag{59}$$

where r is the number of alternatives other than i known, and $\bar{\imath}$ means not-i. Consider the interpretation of (59) just above for the case when we have already calculated, by easy means shown below, $P \, (K = 1)$ and $P \, (K = 1 \text{ and } i)$. These are, respectively, the proportion of people expected to know only one alternative, generally, and the proportion who know only one that is i in particular. Given these calculated, then note that

$$P \, (K = 1) - P \, (K = 1 \text{ and } i) = P \, (K = 1 \text{ and } \bar{\imath})$$
$$= P \, (R = 1 \text{ and } \bar{\imath}) \tag{60}$$

The last row is true because one alternative is known, and since we have excluded that i is known, it is one of the others. So, substituting the left side for $P \, (r \text{ and } \bar{\imath})$ in (59) previously, we obtain

$$[P \, (K = 1) - P \, (K = 1 \text{ and } i)][e^{mp_i/q_i} - 1]$$
$$= P \, (R = 1 \text{ and } i)$$
$$= P \, (K = 2 \text{ and } i) \tag{59a}$$

The last row is true because if one other item is known and i is also known, then in total $K = 2$ are known. After calculating this (59a) for all i, we can then find $P \, (K = 2)$ by

$$P \, (K = 2) = \sum_{i=1}^{n} \frac{P \, (K = 2 \text{ and } i)}{2} \tag{61}$$

because the numerator is the total number of instances known, and dividing by the two instances per person gives the number of people involved, or $P \, (K = 2)$. Now, repeat (60) in this new case:

$$P \, (K = 2) - P \, (K = 2 \text{ and } i) = P \, (K = 2 \text{ and } \bar{\imath})$$
$$= P \, (R = 2 \text{ and } \bar{\imath}) \tag{60a}$$

the last again because, if two in total are known and not i among them, then $R = 2$ or two *others* are known. But this is all we need for (59) to compute $P(R = 2 \text{ and } i)$. That result, by the reasoning given just below (59a), is now equivalent to $P(K = 3 \text{ and } i)$; that is, if two other alternatives and also i are known, then three total are known, and then

$$P(K = 3) = \sum_{i=1}^{n} \frac{P(K = 3 \text{ and } i)}{3}$$

by reasoning like that discussed for (61). And so it proceeds until, one would think, the distribution would end when

$$P(K = k + 1) = 0 \quad \text{and} \quad \sum_{k=0}^{k} P(K = k) = 1 \quad (62)$$

In our examples, the procedure works (and the detailed calculations are about as expected from the data) in the case of M_1, but goes ludicrously awry in the case of M_2, including a violation of the right condition in (62). Two conjectures as to the trouble might be:

1. The sum, $\Sigma P(K = k)$, may not be bounded when the constants, $e^{mp_i/q_i} - 1$, are greater than unity, as they often were with m_2, but not with m_1.

2. If the parameters were not estimated as *exact* solutions to this recursive system, for example, as our m_2 estimates are slightly in error, it might propagate the errors of each $e^{mp/q}$ in calculations with all the others in an explosive manner.

Leaving this problem to another day, the following are other formulas likely to be of use in efficient solutions and/or calculations. First, to start any such recursive method as above, we need $P(K = 0)$ and $P(K = 1)$. The first of these is

$$P(K = 0) = \sum_{M} M \exp\left[-m\left(1 - \prod_{n} q\right)\right] \quad (63)$$

where the product of all the q's in the exponent derives from the considerations given in discussing solutions for parameters. For, what is $P\,(K = 0)$ here would be defined as $Q_{1,2,\ldots,n}$ in that discussion. Because of the earlier simplifying assumption (42) only M_1 is significant, in practice, in (63).

Analogous reasoning leads to an explicit formula for any $P\,(K = 1$ and $i)$, the sum of all of which will be $P\,(K = 1)$:

$$\left.\begin{array}{l} P\,(K = 1 \text{ and } i) \\ P\,(R = 0 \text{ and } i) \end{array}\right\} = \sum_M \sum_{x=1}^{\infty} e^{-m}\frac{m^x}{x!}\,(1 - q_i{}^x)\prod_{j \neq i} q_j{}^x \quad (64)$$

where $\Pi_{j \neq i}$ means the product of all the others except i.

The sum over x yields two e^x series, easy to sum in this case. Then $P\,(K = 1)$ is simply the sum of these over all i. For $P\,(K = 2)$ and so on, however, combinatorial problems arise that make it clearer, if not easier, to compute the analogs to Table 9, and then simply sum entries there for $P\,(K = k)$.

An explicit formula follows for another quantity that is potentially important in calculations and solutions, $E\,(r;i)$, the expected number of other competitive alternatives known when i is known. This, or its companion $E\,(k;i)$, the total number of alternatives known, are sensitive to incorrect parameters and thus should somehow be used in efficient solution methods. For present purposes of finding $E\,(r;i)$, the expected number of competitors known, define a new variable $R\,(j;x)$ as

$$R\,(j;x) = \begin{cases} 1 \text{ if item } j \text{ occurs on } x \text{ exposures} \\ 0 \text{ if otherwise} \end{cases} \quad (j \neq i)$$

Then, given x exposures, the expected *number* of occurrences of all these other alternatives, call it $E\,(r;x)$, would be

$$E\,(r;x) = E\sum_{j \neq i} R\,(j;x) = \sum_{j \neq i} E\,[R\,(j;x)]$$
$$= \sum_{j \neq i} \Pr\,\{R\,(j;x) = 1\} \quad (65)$$

since the probabilities that $R(j;x) = 1$, lower right, give the number of occurrences as well. But this probability on the right for a particular alternative, j, is simply

$$\Pr \{R (j;x) = 1\} = 1 - q_j{}^x \qquad (66)$$

Therefore the sum on the lower right of (65) is obtained by simply adding $n - 1$ terms like (66) for all the alternatives except i:

$$E (r;x) = (n - 1) - \sum_{j \neq i} q_j{}^x \qquad (67)$$

This is, heuristically speaking, an expectation that all $n - 1$ others would have occurred except for the sum of the chances each would fail. Next, one needs this expectation summed over all x, with the proviso in our particular case conveyed by $E (r;i)$, that i must occur as well. Thus, the relevant sum over x is

$$\sum_{x=1}^{\infty} e^{-m} \frac{m^x}{x!} (1 - q_i{}^x) \left[(n - 1) - \sum_{j \neq i} q_j{}^x \right] \qquad (68)$$

which is, as in forming a weighted average, an expected *number* of other items known at each x (in the bracket), weighted by the *probability* that x will occur and i will itself be known at that level of x (the terms preceding the bracket). Expression (68) will have to be divided by the sum of the latter weighting probabilities to get the average in numbers of alternatives. First, to sum (68), it as usual falls into e^x series:

$$\sum_{x=1}^{n} e^{-m} \left[(n - 1)m^x - (n - 1)(mq_i)^x - \sum_{j \neq i} (mq_j)^x \right.$$
$$\left. + \sum_{j \neq i} (mq_i q_j)^x \right] \frac{1}{x!}$$
$$= (n - 1)[1 - e^{-m(1-q_i)}] - \sum_{j \neq i} e^{-m(1-q_j)} + \sum_{j \neq i} e^{-m(1-q_i q_j)} \qquad (69)$$

which is the expected total number of instances of others being known when i is known. For the average per person who knows i, divide by the sum of the people involved, the proportion of people who know i at each x summed over all x, which is simply $1 - e^{-mp_i}$, or the proportion of people expected to know i in total over all x. That division yields

$$E(r;i) = (n-1) - \left[\frac{\sum\limits_{j \neq i} e^{-mp_i} \sum\limits_{j \neq i} e^{-m(1-q_iq_j)}}{1 - e^{-mp_i}} \right] \qquad (70)$$

as the expected number of other competitors known, within any M group, when alternative i is known. Solutions that would satisfy this expression and the marginals for each item, and (62) for all items, would in our experience satisfy everything else.

Note on a

Campaign

Simulator

4

This is a preliminary report on experiments conducted during 1960 with a working model of the formation of opinion in response to election campaign appeals. The model is of the computer simulation type.[1] It does the following:

1. Accepts as initial input a miniature electorate consisting of a 1:1 representation of each respondent in a sample survey
2. Then sets this replica of the electorate "in motion" toward conceivable future states of affairs, with opinions changing or not as a function of:
   a. Internal processes of the model such as discussion and learning

[1]. This academic theory of processes is unrelated to an interesting model of the actual U.S. electorate built by Ithiel Pool and Robert Abelson for the 1960 campaign. Data are acknowledged in the text and, among other collaborators, Charles Higby of the University of Wisconsin was helpful in these tests.

   b. External inputs of new stimuli representing subsequent campaign appeals

3. Until finally the survey population is reported back, along with analytic information, as it would stand on "election day."

4. Such outcomes depend on assumptions (2b), which are next varied, the trial campaign repeated, and so on, thus analyzing the original situation by "realizing" its different dynamic possibilities.[2]

Needless to say, all this is highly experimental. The 1960 tests were made possible by data kindly supplied by Elmo Roper, Inc., who to assist this purpose modified some of its customary procedures in a survey for Columbia Broadcasting System of the Wisconsin Presidential primary between Humphrey, Kennedy, and Nixon.[3] The model has not and will not be used for a party or candidate.

1. TECHNIQUE

We choose for illustration of the technique one major problem on which the 1960 tests with practical data made progress beyond previous academic work on the theory, reported in detail elsewhere.[4] The problem is how an "appeal" or similar event in the external campaign can be represented realistically. That is, how can live content from actual situations be used to characterize the input that, in turn, affects internal processes? About the latter processes, one needs to know only the general idea in Figure 1 for present purposes.

2. The original model was designed for the study of whole electoral systems over long periods. It defines the time period as different elections, for example, every four years instead of, say, every week or two in this case. Extensive reinterpretation of variables is necessary in the shortened time version, but the abstract structure proved retainable.

3. Tests not reported here were also made with 1956 data from the files of the Roper Opinion Research Center, Williams College.

4. In W. McPhee and W. Glaser, eds., *Public Opinion and Congressional Elections* (New York: The Free Press of Glencoe, 1962).

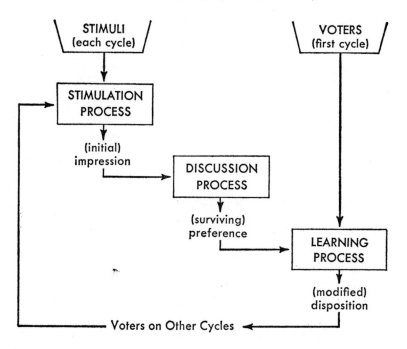

Figure 1

Flow chart of the model.

As Figure 1 suggests, the scheme works so that:

1. "Voters" representing prior survey respondents proceed around an endless loop of response to, discussion of, and further learning from *samples* of new stimuli

2. Which they pick up from a now-developing "campaign," whose new events are represented by changing *distributions* of stimuli that are available for sampling by voters of different groups.

The second point is the problem here and seems not intuitive. The idea is that an appeal or issue or news event is a "distribution" of stimuli. Actually, this is a familiar fact of life in other guises. As one example, suppose we wish to test in a survey the

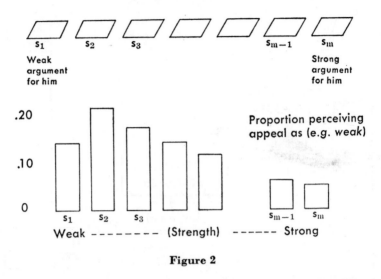

Figure 2

Top: Scale for rating the appeal of an argument for (candidate). *Bottom:* Proportion of people perceiving each such strength of its appeal.

strength of appeal of a given argument for a given cause. Most persons would agree that this requires, if we want to reflect the full variation of appeal that such an argument has for different people, some kind of scale of gradation as along the top of Figure 2. Then a person indicates on the scale how compelling he perceives this argument to be in behalf of cause X.

Over many people, answers are dispersed, as counted at the bottom of Figure 2. Thus, the notion of "the" appeal of an argument is actually *many* appeals, a distribution. For reasons made evident below, call this a "perceptual dispersion."

Next, while the connection between the two is ordinarily not drawn, there is another idea familiar in survey analysis that illustrates what is meant by the "effect" of such an appeal. As one example, consider how poll analysts predict "turnout" in response to the election attraction. They make an index locating people along a general scale of disposition to vote. Then they establish a cutting point, above which the sample is treated as representative of voters, below nonvoters. For our purposes this is the same as giving the former probability 1 and the latter 0 of responding. Pollers know this is a simplification and that there is actually a sequence of increasing probabilities of voting as one proceeds up the scale.[5] Call this sequence, some function of the basic disposition, a "response curve."

The *form* of this function, while it probably always increases monotonically with increasing disposition, is obviously conditional on the stimulus situation. If the appeal is great, for example, a Roosevelt or Eisenhower on the ticket, then "fair weather friends" of the party come out in unusual numbers. That is, the response curve bulges up at low and intermediate disposition levels, where it is ordinarily undependable. Whereas on a rainy day with a dull contest, the curve is concave. "Only the diehards" at high disposition levels respond with high probability. Lazarsfeld calls these different functions evoked by different stimulus items "trace lines," but for present purposes they are best referred to as *conditional* response functions; that is, functions of the disposition but in a way that is conditional on the stimulus situation. Figure 3 gives idealized examples, of which the vertical is the (smoothed) curve of probabilities of response at different disposition levels.

Now, what one of the three processes of the model, the "stimulation process," accomplishes as its contribution to the total is to *connect* the two problems above. It takes as input "appeals" that are actually distributions of stimuli that vary in their perceived cogency. Then the "impressions" that voters gain from sampling these stimuli are, when aggregated, varying forms of a function of the basic disposition, for example, of general party tendency. This basic disposition is always controlling. (All variants are some monotonic function of it.) But the idea of the "effect" of a stimulus situation is to change the *form* of the response curve in favorable or unfavorable ways.

5. See the papers by H. Freeman and W. Glaser in *Public Opinion and Congress Elections, op. cit.*

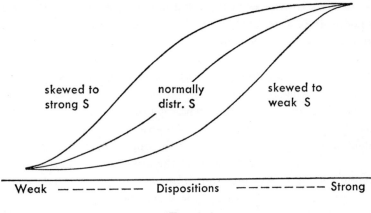

skewed to strong S   normally distr. S   skewed to weak S

Weak — — — — — — Dispositions — — — — — — Strong

Figure 3

Response functions from *s* distributions.

The mechanism that elicits a single response for each indi-vidual voter was designed without such any explicit statistical connection in mind. Its assumption is like that revealed in Gutt-man scales.[6] The weaker the person's disposition, the stronger the attraction needed to elicit a "yes" impression. The stronger the disposition, the weaker the attraction needed and thus the *more* stimulus items that would be acceptable (or more likely a single random stimulus encountered will be acceptable, since in the model they are only sampled, one at a time).

An aggregate statistical version of these individual assump-tions, however, better reveals the remarkably simple connection between dispersion of appeal and form of response. Assume that a broad appeal is presented to various people, for example, Sena-tor Humphrey stressed the "farm" issue as an appeal in his behalf to Wisconsin people in 1960. Assume that this is not the same stimulus for each person, but different stimuli of different cogency

6. See, as a widely available reference, Guttman's contribution in *Measurement and Prediction*, Vol. IV of the series, "Studies in Social Psy-chology in World War II," Samuel A. Stouffer, ed. (Princeton, N.J.: Prince-ton University Press, 1950).

as arguments for the given cause. Let this appeal be a random variable, s, that could take values between 0 and 1, the values being grades of attractiveness or cogency as an argument for the cause. The sample space might be thought of as continuous, if one wishes, but empirical cases would tend to cluster in discrete gradations, m in number, $s = 0 \le s = s_1 < s = s_2 = \cdots < s = s_m \le 1.0$, in order of attractiveness or acceptability.

In many applications, this variation would be due to the variable attractiveness of different *interpretations* that can be placed on the stimulus content, as different people see it in their sampling of the news. For example, in social distance scales and perhaps in an actual civil rights issue in the South, the idea of "Negroes and whites eating together" could strike some people as an argument about eating together in restaurants, others about eating together at home. Persons with little disposition to be friendly to the opposite race would accept only the former, while those of friendlier disposition would accept either.

The higher the disposition, the more grades of interpretation would be acceptable. Therefore, define these gradations in conjunction with a corresponding classification of people's disposition levels, p, also between 0 and 1. Since the higher p is, the more stimuli would be acceptable, define the top gradation, where *all* m stimuli would be, as $p = p_m$ (with $p_m \le 1.0$). Define the next lower disposition as one where all but the weakest stimulus, $s = s_1$, would be acceptable, and call it $p = p_{m-1}$. And so on down by decreasing disposition, $p = p_{m-2} > p = p_{m-3} > \cdots > p = p_{m-m} \ge 0$, where no stimulus would be acceptable.

Then, if persons of different dispositions are exposed to stimuli or interpretations of different strength, the rule is the same as in Guttman scales. This is made intuitive in Table 1. For the record, a (rather nonintuitive) formal version of Table 1 is:

$$\begin{aligned}
&\text{If } s = s_i \text{ and } p = p_{m-j}, \text{ then} \\
&i > j \text{ implies: yes, acceptable} \\
&i \le j \text{ implies: no, not acceptable}
\end{aligned} \tag{1}$$

Table 1

Rule for Accepting Perceived Appeal

			Appeal				
			Weak			Strong	
		s_0	s_1	s_2	$\cdots$	s_{m-1}	s_m
Strong	p_m		OK	OK		OK	OK
	p_{m-1}			OK		OK	OK
	.						
Disposition	.						
	.						
	p_2					OK	OK
Weak	p_1						OK
	p_0						

We account for the observed error in real scales and for probabilistic answers generally, for example, in latent-structure analysis, by noting that in the empirical world those methods must try to measure response to one "whole" appeal. Whereas that appeal is here visualized as a set of substimuli, and we postulate that people only *sample* from all such possible subinterpretations.[7]

When a homogenous social group samples from the same array of such substimuli, let $s = s_i$ occur with probability x_i. For example, in sampling the news, x_i might be the frequency of "exposure" of people to interpretations at this ith level of attractiveness. Then an over-all appeal is a set of such frequencies, $F(s)$, where $F(s) = x_1, x_2, x_3, \ldots, x_m$. For example, $F(s)$ might be a normal dispersion around some mean s value.

By the assumptions above, the probability of "yes," or acceptable answers, $P(y;p_j)$, at each level of disposition, p_j, would be a simple sequence:

$$P(y;p_1) = x_m$$
$$P(y;p_2) = x_m + x_{m-1}$$

7. This implies that if we really knew what people were responding to, e.g., as Asch used to question experimental subjects about what they perceived the stimulus content to mean, that response would *not* be stochastic. People answer "as they see it" (to what they see).

$$P\ (y;p_3) = x_m + x_{m-1} + x_{m-2}$$

.

.

.

$$P\ (y;p_m) = x_m + x_{m-1} + \cdots + x_2 + x_1$$

This function is the abstraction in the model corresponding to a "response curve" in real data. We see the simple way it depends on the abstraction, $F(s)$, a concept very close to the distributions earlier called "perceptual dispersions" in real data. The former is simply a *cumulative* version of the frequencies, or probabilities, of the latter.[8] But it is accumulated "backwards," starting with the probabilities of high stimuli that are the only ones cogent to persons at the low end of the disposition scale. For example, Figure 3 showed how skewed distributions of many *high* or compelling *s* bring out the "fair weather friends" at *lower* dispositions. In contrast, "only the diehard" very high on the basic disposition still responds well when $F(s)$ is such that lower or weaker *s* are most common.

Both the p_i and the s_i are technically unobservables; but a fair approximation to the former, the location of people relative to one another along a disposition scale, is provided by scaling methods. Latent structure was used.[9] Table 2 illustrates how it converts a person's answers to five or more qualitative questions (with + yes, − no, in the table) into a relative location along the disposition scale.

The stimulus distributions $F(s)$ are the problem. One each is needed for each appeal as it bears on each candidate, within each

8. Technically the *distribution* (cumulative) *function,* reversed to start at the high levels, if the expected frequencies $x_1, x_2, \ldots$ were approximated by some function of s, as we imply they could be by the notation $F(s)$.

9. With $p_i =$ "probability of being in class I" assigned to people responding in a given pattern, in Lazarsfeld's two-class model described in *Measurement and Prediction, op. cit.* Different but comparable scales are made for *each* candidate or party. For example, disposition to party B is not just the complement of that to party A, although empirically that tends to be so.

Table 2

How Patterns of Answers Locate People along a Disposition Scale

Answers of Persons

Question	i	j	k	
1	+	+	+	
2	+	−	+	
3	−	+	+	
4	−	−	−	
5	−	−	+	
.	.	.	.	
.	.	.	.	
.	.	.	.	
p_0	p_i	p_j	p_k	p_m

homogenous demographic group, of which 20 groups were used in stratifying Wisconsin. The mechanically best raw data from which to postulate the form of such a stimulus distribution, to use as input to a given group in the model, are the dispersions of answers obtained when *real* members of the corresponding group in a prior survey were asked to rate how the given appeal struck them as an argument for the given cause (on scales like that shown in Figure 2 earlier).[10]

Answers cannot be used in the raw, of course. All such distributions of answers are averaged. This average is then equated with a "standard" distribution of $F(s)$ that is known to bring out the best possible response function we can postulate in the absence of other information (the expected values when the p_i are used as if probabilities).[11] Then every particular distribution of

10. This mechanically ideal form of data is being approached in recent work since Wisconsin. In that case, to cover a wider range of issues compactly, questions of the kind "Which candidate is best for (farm, etc.)?" were used. The answers can be transformed only into linear $F(s)$.

11. This obviously has to be kept in mind in choice of scale. The p_i used, "probabilities of being in Class I" in Lazarsfeld's two-class model, were tested by Murray Gendell as to their correspondence to subsequent turnout probabilities in a panel study of the 1950 election. The correspondence is not systematically bad. In practice, the results in 1956 and 1960 tests were not significantly different from poll predictions based on the same data.

perceptions, of each argument for each cause rated by every group separately, is expressed as a set of deviations from the empirical average. These deviations are then transformed into a corresponding set of deviations from the "standard" $F(s)$. Absolute scale connecting p's and s's is unknown.[12] But since the set of p's is the same for all appeals, the variation in each's effect is almost wholly due to how the survey respondents in each and every group perceived it to differ from other test appeals. Thus, *relative* effect of different appeals is here an issue not substantially different from survey validity generally.[13]

2. AN ILLUSTRATIVE PROBLEM

Figures 4 and 5 give a very brief illustration of some results. The purpose is to study dynamics, in the model but reflecting what official returns in Wisconsin indicated was necessary to get from the original survey situation, almost a month before, to the final vote.

Since it was legal to cross over into either primary, without registration, we treat it as a three-way race. The chief change was a disappearance of 25–30 per cent of the intended vote in the Republican column where Nixon was uncontested, a drop from about 40 per cent to under 30 per cent of the total.[14] In each figure along the bottom is shown this Nixon percentage of the three-way vote. The vertical here happens to be the Humphrey percentage. Thus, a point defines these two votes at any time, and their differ-

12. One can change it to make response to all appeals "livelier" or "stickier," but cannot influence the relative response to different issues differently, which is determined empirically as above.

13. For example, in tests with both 1956 and 1960 data the model drew no conclusions about the relative effect of different issues not plainly evident in the original surveys used. The model adds something only where there are further complications, as in the differential response of 20 different groups to a three-way contest in the Nixon-Humphrey example below.

14. Roper made the survey prior to the main campaigning and, of course, did not attempt to say what would happen to the uncontested Nixon vote. (Nixon did not campaign.)

ence from 100 per cent is the Kennedy vote. (Since Kennedy opposed Humphrey, his direction is down.) Movements across the plane represented by the arrows are the *changes* in the vote division, reported by the model. For instance, the start of each arrow is the model's best estimate as of the original survey (although N's are only 20 to 50 cases in any one such homogeneous group).

The test problem shown is one which, in principle, could have been fully analyzed before the election, because it was plainly impending. It is the question:

What would happen if the Democratic contest were "heated up" by using Humphrey's and Kennedy's strongest appeals, while simultaneously *weakening Nixon* as an attraction? That is, if we relax one of the three forces in a previously "taut" situation (most votes committed), which of the other two would now benefit?

This was simulated for all candidates in all 20 population groups simultaneously, but we illustrate the best situation for the underdog, Humphrey. Figure 3 shows Humphrey's strongest group, farmers in his bastion of the northwest half of the state. And the issue that Kennedy and Humphrey are stressing in this illustrative model run is also Humphrey's best—"farm" appeal. Given ideal circumstances, he runs away with the vote. (The upper arrow moves dramatically to the upper left, which is high for Humphrey and low for Kennedy and Nixon.)

And these ideal circumstances were indeed realized for him in this group, in part, in the actual election. This is shown by the asterisks or X's on Figure 4. Each is a precinct vote in the official election.[15] The precincts contained comparable types of people (farmers) in the same part of the state. The X precincts suggest a response much like the model's: where Nixon's hold on certain normally Republican groups was relaxed, paradoxically it

15. All relevant precincts from an analysis carried out with detailed demographic data by historian Lee Benson for other purposes.

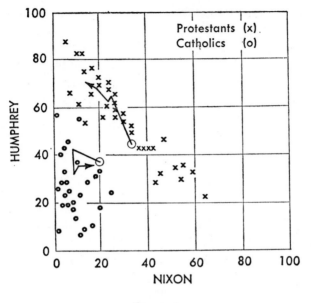

Figure 4

Humphrey farm issue among farmers in northwestern Wisconsin.

was Humphrey who benefited. Why didn't he forge ahead, then, when the Nixon vote relaxed, as it did in the real campaign as well?

As Humphrey's first problem, note that the upper arrows in each chart and the related X precincts concern Protestants only. The lower arrow (model) and the open circles (precincts) are Catholics. The latter went to Kennedy even under the ideal circumstances we set in motion here for Humphrey. And in virtually all groups over the state, the model and the official precincts showed much the same. Next, as a second and more serious problem for Humphrey, now consider Figure 5. It is selected exactly to match the groups in the first. The one difference is that these are now middle-class rural townspeople. They are similar to farmers except that, unlike farmers but like most other Repub-

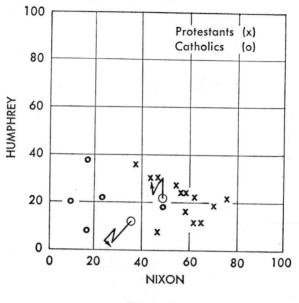

Figure 5

Humphrey farm issue among town middle class in northwestern Wisconsin.

lican groups in the state, they did not have such an immediate stake in the "farm" problem of 1960 that was Humphrey's strongest appeal and that he stressed in the real campaign (and in this model run). Among such people, the farm issue, and indeed most Humphrey appeals, tended not to "go anywhere." For, other than what Humphrey already had, the remaining Protestants were mostly traditional Republican types. They held, weak appeal or not, for *Nixon.* (Both model arrow and precincts stayed to the low right center.)[16]

16. No pretense at "fit" is made, and these illustrations chosen for other reasons are a little *better* than the average. A crude test of portraying dynamics would be for the model to move closer to the precincts in the 20 subgroups than the survey a month before. The model would "pass" this test well, but *only* by choosing its stimuli in the light of the outcome (weak Nixon and selected strong Humphrey appeals to go with the generally strong Kennedy appeals).

In a greater or a usually somewhat lesser degree all over the state, this same situation was revealed: Humphrey was in a "squeeze" between Kennedy and Nixon. With Kennedy holding much of the Catholic vote and getting more with each move, Humphrey's potential was in the remaining Protestant vote. But most of that is normally *Republican,* and thus the presence of Nixon on the ballot tied down the other main bloc of votes, the only major exception being farmers[17] like those shown in Figure 3 and to a lesser degree urban lower-income Protestants. Humphrey fell, then, between two blocs.

As a result, the net outcome of the test problem above was that the weakening of the Nixon appeal released a (high) proportion of Republican Catholics for Kennedy that almost exactly matched a (lower) proportion of the more numerous Protestant groups who were less willing to leave Nixon for Humphrey. Thus, even though the total cross over party lines in the final weeks was perhaps 25–30 per cent of the original Nixon vote—at least 10–12 per cent of the total—it left the statewide ratio between Kennedy and Humphrey almost exactly the same![18]

Judging from the vote versus the survey, there was also little net trend in that two-way ratio in Wisconsin either. Therefore, a lot of "dynamics" went nowhere, in the net trend, a result that is, if disappointing, realistic.

17. A model that shows "what could be" also suggests "what might have been." The chief potential of the latter kind was, by every indication, an impending farm revolt against the Republicans in 1960, muted later by the nomination of Kennedy. Usually Protestant farmers were the most volatile in leaving the Republicans, but least went to Kennedy. So any Republican feeling that Kennedy's eastern vote later in 1960 was fortuitous might equally subtract some of the GOP's compensating farm states.

18. The only dramatic potentials for net change were, with choice of appeals unfavorable to Humphrey, for him to take a bad beating as he subsequently did in West Virginia. The model, incidentally, is mechanically able to generate a West Virginia or any other known population's vote from responses of corresponding persons in Wisconsin. If it had, however, many runs would have been wrong. (Protestants in West Virginia voted much more for Kennedy.)

On the Logic

of Addiction

5

There was a time when "addiction" meant dependence on opiates and only that. Yet there are good reasons for treating it as a much more general idea, for example, as "contagion" has been generalized as a logical idea (in contagious process models) of far wider applicability than its name implies. In the first place, medicine itself is finding that the strict addiction idea covers an increasingly general class of problems. For example, the World Health Organization has finally had to admit alcoholism as not "just an analogy" to addiction but itself a distinct type.[1] No doubt problems like smoking and obesity will force recognition of still different physical types. There is a need for logical clarity about what addiction means in each case. At the same time, there are so many psychological and social phenomena in modern life

1. See in E. M. Jellinek, *The Disease Concept of Alcoholism* (New Haven, Center for Alcohol Studies, Yale University, 1960).

that can be given no other reasonable name in any dictionary—from addiction to work to hobbies that become addictive work—that it seems pointless to continue to dismiss such important problems as "only analogies" to addiction. Instead, we investigate the latter for what it is—as any good analogy is—a very general *logical* idea.

The original problem of addiction to narcotics, in fact, is one that the writer is not competent to discuss as more than an illustration. While those familiar with that problem can no doubt interpret the logic for their own purposes, we concentrate on two other examples: (1) social and personal addictions of the kind we call "enthusiasms" or "passions," for example chess or golf, and especially intellectual "pursuits," and (2) similar results that have physiological components, but unlike chronic addiction are "explosive" and "runaway" phenomena, as in drunkenness and alcoholism.

The particular model with which we begin exploration of the problem here is simple enough to be clear to the nontechnical reader, to whom we address the paper with concrete interpretations throughout the text. We suggest that he can skip most of the subsequent mathematical details once he has an understanding, which *is* essential, of the notation and model.[2]

1. DEFINITIONS

The logic consists of only two variables and three parameters. (The latter are conditions that govern how the variables behave.) None are meant to be specific "things," but classifications of the general *kinds* of forces at work in all addictive problems. The two variables, for example, stand for the two kinds of behavior that are always of concern:

2. This model and current bibliographic work on the physiological implications to be reported elsewhere were made possible by National Science Foundation Grant No. 13045.

C = "consumption" = rate of doing the thing to which one may become addicted, for example, number of times chess is played a week or number of cigarettes smoked per day

E = "effect" of this activity = pleasures or utilities that the consumption achieves, for example, such and such a golf score or so much pleasure from opiates

Of the two, the first is usually observed or measured objectively and the second solved for only indirectly. Indeed, in this particular paper, E, or effect, will play only an heuristic role and disappear in solutions expressed in C, or consumption, alone. But one could turn the model around to have E the observed behavior, for example, a succession of changing golf scores, and then infer C as the unobserved activity that had gone into producing, say, the improvement.

Next, the parameters (conditions) governing the behavior of these variables are, in effect, a classification of the kinds of motivational forces postulated in theories of addiction. The classification is based logically on *to what variable* each parameter applies:

s = "stimulation" = any motivation toward consumption that applies in proportion that one is *not* consuming, for example, stress after withdrawal of consumption or renewed desire to play tennis because one has not played for several days

r = "resistance" = any motivation against consumption that applies in proportion that one *has* been consuming, for example, satiation and nausea in drinking and expense and time in addictive hobbies

a = "acceleration" = any motivation toward consumption that applies in proportion to rate of *change* in consumption, for example, as effect of increases in alcohol in the blood is to increase drinking, or improvement from increased practice of a sport is to increase play of the sport

These parameters may have both positive or negative signs or be zero (not operative). For example, $-s$ is a negative stimulation in proportion that one is *not* doing the consuming activity.

Table 1

Examples of the Parameters

Given Parameter (Kind of Cause) Applies in Proportion to:

	Lack of Consumption	Consumption	Change in Consumption
Its Consequence Is to: Increase Consumption	$+s$ E.g., "withdrawal stress"; "absence makes the heart grow fonder"	$-r$ E.g., "negative resistance"; "insatiability"	$+a$ E.g., release of inhibitions"; "one drink leads to another"
Decrease Consumption	$-s$ E.g., "out of sight out of mind"; "abstinence" therapy	$+r$ E.g. "satiation"; physical "limits"; "intolerance"	$-a$ E.g., "keeping up"; "keeping down"; "conforming" behavior

It expresses in social affairs the idea "out of sight, out of mind." In physical addictions like smoking, $-s$ expresses the idea that prolonged abstinence kills off the desire to consume. These possibilities are illustrated in Table 1 and Figures 1 to 3.

With all these negative (not to mention zero) and positive possibilities, it is difficult to think of *any* relevant motivational force not so classifiable. For example, psychiatric theories of the "release" type (from tensions, and so forth), often given as explanation for why one drink releases motivation for another drink in alcoholism, clearly belong in the $+a$ category (whereby consumption accelerates itself).

2. ASSUMPTIONS

The fact that release accelerating consumption does *not* have the consequence it is usually intended to "explain" in alcoholism, as we shall see, illustrates that no matter how oversimplified the model below has to be, it could not be so oversimplified as the usual case—having classificatory concepts alone and no

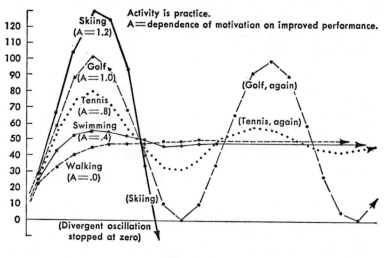

Figure 1

The "unstabilizing" effect of $a = A$ ($s = .2$, $r = .2$). Activity is C_t.

means at all to explore the consequences. The model now proposed has only that intellectual purpose for us. It is not to pretend behavior "is" this simple. It is to learn what are the unobvious consequences of even the most obvious assertions that *we* can make in the above categories.

For example, the first of two relationships in the model is called the "intrinsic effect" equation. Let ΔE_t be the *change* in effect starting at time t. Then assume as explained below that we let E, the "effect" of consumption, be scaled so that the normal range is from 0 to 1. Therefore, $1 - E$ is the "room" for further effect of consumption. Then assume

$$\Delta E_t = a(1 - E_t)(\Delta C_{t-1}) \tag{1}$$

which says that

> some proportion, a
> of the room for further effect, $1 - E$
> is converted by changes in consumption, ΔC
> into changes in effect, ΔE

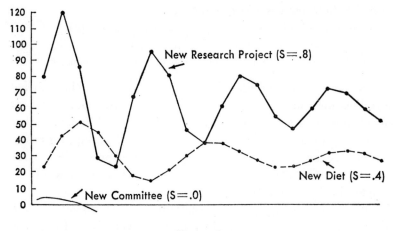

Figure 2

An "amplitude" effect of $s = S$ on oscillating C_t (a equals .8. r equals .4).

A simplification will now introduce the second equation, governing C, the "consumption" equation. There are initially only two parameters in it. One is s, or stimulation of all kinds to *increase* consumption, other than the effect of consumption itself in motivating its own further increase. The other parameter is r, or resistance of all kinds toward *decreasing* consumption, other than the effect of decreasing consumption itself on its own increase-decrease. If we omit temporarily the latter, self-generated change then the increments in consumption, ΔC, can be simplified to

$$\Delta C_t = s(1 - C_t) - r(C_t) \qquad (2)$$

where we now make C also vary within a "normal" range from 0 consumption to 1, the latter being normal maximum. This maximum can be exceeded, but only with peril. (For example in alcoholism, $C = 1$ would be the 0.15 per cent blood level that defines drunken driving in many states.) What expression (2) says is that change in consumption, ΔC, is the net balance of

stimulants to increase, in proportion *s*
applied to the available "room" to increase consumption, $1 - C$
minus resistance toward decrease, in proportion *r*
applied to the available consumption that can decrease, *C*

If the words sound like physics, it is only to give the abstract symbols meanings that are neutral to the actual psychiatry or biochemistry or sociology, or whatever is involved. Instead, what matters here is the formal *structure* of the relationship, for example, where we group as *s* whatever applies in proportion to the available room for further consumption, $1 - C$ and as *r* whatever applies in proportion to *C*.

One of the defining ideas in addiction has not yet entered and does now as a complication in the actual version of the above simplification. It is that the above extrinsic stimulants to consumption, *s*, are increased by an *intrinsic* effect of the intake itself, which we will temporarily call *i*. And the above extrinsic resistance to consumption, *r*, is decreased also by effect of consumption itself, which for theoretic simplicity we will consider the same *i*, the intrinsic effect of intake (as qualitatively it indeed is). The symbol, *i*, will shortly be eliminated, but the equation with the above assumptions added gives the essential idea:

$$\Delta C_t = (s + i)(1 - C_t) - (r - i)(C_t) \qquad (2a)$$

This is the same as before, but with *i* added to stimulants and *i* taken away from resistances. We now define *i* or the "intrinsic effect" as

$$i = \frac{\Delta E}{1 - E} \qquad (1b)$$

$$= a(\Delta C)$$

These are components of the earlier "effect" equation numbered (1), and the fact that either definition is equivalent to the other is true algebraically from (1). When each, the upper or lower above, is, respectively, substituted for *i* in the consumption equa-

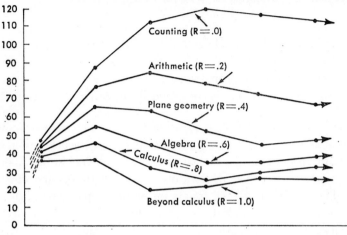

Illustrative activity is the proportion of students who, after sampling the subject, continue learning activity.

Figure 3

A "reversing" effect of $r = R$ in paths with monotonic tendencies (a equals .4, s equals .4). Illustrative activity is C_t.

tion (2a), the upper one lends itself to what might be called "clinical" and the lower to "behavioristic" interpretations of intrinsic motivation. The clinical version, using the upper definition above, interprets the intrinsic motivation by some further theory about what E, or the effect, is. When E is substituted in the consumption equation, for i, what influences consumption is the *relative increase* in this E effect, its increments as a proportion of the remaining room for effect before some kind of saturation.

The other version of the consumption equation arises from the "behavioristic" definition above, $i = a(\Delta C)$. Substituted for i, this equation says it does not know anything about physiological or psychological "effects," but observes something like *acceleration* in the early to middle phases of growth of consumption. The technical reader can see this better by making the actual substitution:

$$\Delta C_t = [s + a(\Delta C_{t-1})](1 - C_t) - [r - a(\Delta C_{t-1})](C_t) \quad (2b)$$

where time subscripts now become important, $t - 1$ being the previous period. What it says is, for example, in the *left* bracket:

the stimulants, s
working in proportion to the potential that consumption can still be increased, $1 - C$
are increased by some proportion, a
of the recent increase in consumption itself, ΔC_{t-1}

In the right bracket of expression (2b), normal cautions and resistance, r, are analogously decreased by any acceleration in consumption, for example, by the increase in alcohol in the blood.

The present framework does not say these things are *always* true. The condition $a = 0$, found for some people, would mean that their consumption rate is externally decided, irrelevant to its own recent changes. An example is French wine drinking. And minus a would be "polite" conformity. It would portray increases that provoke their own reduction, presumably because the person observes too much effect and "cuts down"—equation (1) with $-a$. But then decreases would instigate their own increases, and one would thereby "keep up." Therefore, it is an *empirical* question what value of a and s and r (estimated from behavior patterns by formulas given in the Technical Note) will fit a given person's behavior in given situations. The model itself, for all its involved motivation above, can be shown to be effectively *neutral* logic, not "theory" in the sense of speculation.[3]

3. What we mean is, for example, if a statistician or mathematical psychologist were to discard all our E and i and similar postulates as one man's opinion and instead look at the most *neutral* model they could think of that would still permit deduction, they would probably choose

$$\Delta C = s(1 - C) \pm r(C) + a(\Delta C_{t-1})$$

or simply the addition of the different sources from which change could arise. But we are astonished to find that, after routine algebraic manipulation, our model comes down to this! (See Technical Note.)

3. TYPES OF CONSEQUENCES

Now consider more closely the notion that C, or consumption, is scaled so that "normal" is between $C = 0$ and $C = 1$. The latter, normal maximum, would be defined in a given field as the consumption that, if exceeded, would be something beyond the "harmless" addictions of normal life. For example, in addiction to a leisure pursuit, $C = 1$ would be using all one's available spare time for it, and $C > 1$ would then begin to interfere with work, family, and so forth. Here, as in most social interpretations, $C = 1$ would be some rate of activity per week or month; but in interpretations of the model as physical addiction, the time period would usually be observations during a single consumption *episode*, for example, every hour of the day. Then $C = 1$ is the maximum level at any one time that is considered medically safe, for example 0.15 per cent alcohol in the blood or comparable dose of some narcotic. A typical meaning, whatever the particular definition, is that below this level the person can stop when he wishes, above it, stopping is problematic.

Now, what the model produces is a *path* of consumption that stays within or goes outside these normal bounds. While varying combinations of parameters lead to an almost infinite variety of such consumption paths, the main types of concern here are classified by the *final* outcome:

Normal = may temporarily exceed 1, but reaches equilibrium within $1 > C > 0$, for example, settles down to less than a pack a day of cigarettes

Abortive = quickly returns to $C = 0$, for example, failure to learn difficult hobbies like chess, tennis

Aversive = reaches equilibrium below $0 > C$, for example, the former addict of Communism now active in anti-Communism

Chronic = reaches equilibrium above $C > 1$, for example, the drug addict and the French chronic alcoholic never sober but never hopelessly drunk

Explosive = rises too rapidly above $C > 1$, then suddenly collapses toward $0 > C$, for example, ordinary drunkenness or short-lived "passions"

Divergent = carried away toward consumption ever rising beyond any bounds and without return, for example, drinking to unconsciousness and hospitalization

The major problem here is to diagnose how the logical causes of these kinds of path differ among themselves and from those of normal consumption (see Figure 4).

The sense in which one can diagnose "logical causes," without knowing the precise mechanism, can be illustrated in the simplest case: the abortive start. This is some happy accident of youth for many an adult nonsmoker, not to mention the person who survives hospital opiates without addiction. But it is any unhappy problem in adult education and recreation. The bulk of the population cannot enjoy the skilled pursuits like tennis, golf, chess, music, and painting, because of abortive starts in the initial "becoming an addict" that it really takes to learn such difficult things in the first place.

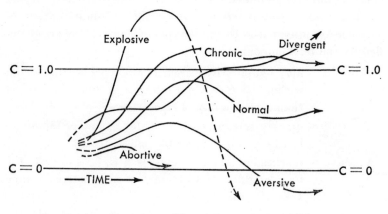

Figure 4

Types of consumption path.

Herbert A. Simon, in his brief but interesting "Berlitz model," reaches the conclusion that to avoid such abortive starts on difficult learning tasks requires extrinsic motivation at first, as a pump requires priming. An example is enforced study. The present model reaches the same conclusion, with a supplementary interpretation as follows. The appended Technical Note shows how equation (2), when it is specified with $\Delta C_t = C_{t+1} - C_t$ and with intrinsic motivation,

$$i = a(\Delta C_{t-1}) = a(C_t - C_{t-1})$$

simplifies to the basic difference equation:

$$C_{t+1} = (1 + a - s - r)C_t - aC_{t-1} + s \qquad (3)$$

Now suppose a learner is just getting started; that is, the period is $t = 1$, and we want the expected activity for $t + 1$, that is, C_2. For this purpose, rewrite equation (3) as

$$C_2 = (1 - s - r)C_1 + a(C_1 - C_0) + s \qquad (4)$$

Note that the first term on the right is something like the inertia, or carryover, of activity from C_1 now into C_2. This carryover would be substantially less than 1 and thus less than the full C_1, however. Therefore, the path would turn back *down* again if it depended on this term alone. We ask of the other terms on the right, then, how might they save the day? Reading from the far right, we have, first, s, or "situational stimuli" of an external sort motivating activity when there is not any. Then, $C_1 - C_0$ is the initial "pushoff" of activity from $C_0 = 0$. For example, it is the initial playing of tennis that interests one in playing tennis. These forces must be supplied externally, and this illustrates Simon's conclusion that something beyond "self-starting" is needed to keep the process off the ground.

Note, however, that the initial pushoff of activity is *mulliplied* by a. It will be recalled that this is the degree to which activity has a noticeable effect that then motivates more activity. In learning interpretations of a, it would be like "ability," that is, ability to convert initial activity immediately into self-rewarding progress. In sports, for example, there is the natural athlete who can quickly get onto the idea of a new game; in mental activities there is the "natural intellectual" who quickly picks new skills and new research interests.

Now, the latter kind of person is often equally infamous as a "dilettante" and the former an an "ex-athlete"; that is, they *drop* interests quickly as well. One reason is already evident: picking up new activities easily, they pick up too many. But a more diabolical reason will become evident later: the very ability a, which is essential to get started, will turn out when the activity matures, to have been shifting sand on which to build an enduring interest.

4. THE SOLUTION

To see this it is necessary to consider more extended paths of consumption, that is, successively C_1, C_2, C_3, . . . , C_n, where n is a large number of periods. These paths can and have been run out in a computer with equation (3), from which typical results are illustrated in the figures interspersed through the preceding text. But to consider general types of consumption paths, like those above, it is better to work with an algebraic solution. By a "solution" is meant here an expression for consumption, C_k, in any future period, k. The appended Technical Note discusses how C_k in such difference equations is given by a formula that, although the reason is *not* intuitive, has a simple structure:

$$C_k = c_1 m_1{}^k + c_2 m_2{}^k + \frac{s}{s + r} \qquad (5)$$

where the new symbols like m will be defined below. For the moment, the key thing to note is the *form;* namely, there are a number of constants not dependent on the time period, the c's, the m's and $s/(s + r)$. The only "dynamic" force over time is the way the m's are raised to successively higher powers over time, since $k =$ time period. In particular, c_1 and c_2 are arbitrary constants that serve only to specify the starting points of any particular path of consumption and are not important except in special problems like the "pushoff" in abortive starts above. Therefore, we relegate them to the Technical Note and deal with the main expression:

$$C_k = m_1{}^k + m_2{}^k + \frac{s}{s+r} \qquad (k \text{ large}) \qquad (5a)$$

This equation makes it obvious that the whole outcome is going to depend on what magnitudes and signs are given to m_1 and m_2 in their definition, which will be derived below from the parameters (causal conditions). But first note the crucial ideas:

If both m's are less than 1, they will diminish over time and finally disappear. For example, $m = .8$ follows the sequence .8, .64, .51, .41, . . . , so the path will converge on the constant $s/(s + r)$ as the final steady state.

If either m is above 1, the opposite will occur and the solution diverge. For example, if $m = 1.2$, the sequence will be 1.20, 1.44, 1.73, . . . , overriding not only the steady state but any bounds.

If either m is negative, it will contribute an *oscillatory* component to the path of consumption. For example, if $m = -.8$, then $(-.8)^2 = +.64$, but $(-.8)^3 = -.51$, and so on. Whereas, a positive m contributes a monotonic (unswerving) component. If we mix the two, typical paths go one way for a time and then reverse.

Whichever m is larger in absolute magnitude will *dominate* in the path. For example, if both are less than 1, the larger m will give the early path its main character and be the last to disappear. And if both are more than 1, the larger will grow at the faster rate.

The earlier types of consumption paths in addiction can be translated into these terms. For example, if both m_1 and m_2 are less than 1, the path finally reaches an equilibrium, and if $s/(s + r)$ is between 1 and 0, it is a "normal" equilibrium. A program to analyze what causes different types of paths of addictive consumption, then, is in formal terms to analyze what determines the magnitudes and signs of the m's.

Unfortunately, their definition in the model is not intuitive; but, as the Technical Note shows, the two m's are the two solutions for the quadratic equation:

$$m^2 + (s + r - 1 - a)m + a = 0 \qquad (6)$$

Therefore, we have the quadratic formula:

$$m = \frac{-(s + r - 1 - a) \pm \sqrt{(s + r - 1 - a)^2 - 4a}}{2} \qquad (7)$$

where we will call the result from a plus sign before the radical, m_1, and that from a minus sign before the radical, m_2. As unintelligible as this concept seems at first glance, it will now lend itself to proofs that make quite concrete when and why a particular kind of addictive consumption path will result.

5. TYPES OF PATHS

Normal

What is called "normal drinking" behavior illustrates the typical path of this type; for example, it may oscillate up rather "high" at first but damps down toward a steady state safely between 0 and 1. "Normal" means it reaches the latter equilibrium and not necessarily that the behavior is "usual," since in narcotic consumption almost no one can find an equilibrium within medically safe limits. Yet the pathology in drug addiction is, curiously enough, not explosive nor divergent consumption. It is chronic; that is, there *is* an equilibrium or steady state. Therefore, the pathology in drug addiction must be that it violates the first and most obvious requirement for normal consumption—that the steady state be *within* the safe bounds, 0 to 1.

Now, this steady state, the one and only equilibrium point in the model, is found as follows. Texts show it is a value for consumption, C, which when substituted in the consumption equation (3) for C_{t-1} and C_t leads to a calculated C_{t+1} that is unchanged, that is,

$$C_{t+1} = C_t = C_{t-1} = C$$

This condition is satisfied in the present model only by

$$C = \frac{s}{s + r} \qquad (C \neq 0) \tag{8}$$

Hence, the first and most obvious requirement for reaching a normal equilibrium between 0 and 1 is that

$$1 > \frac{s}{s + r} > 0 \tag{9}$$

What happens when all other conditions for stability are met except this one is discussed under chronic and aversive paths below. What matters for normal behavior is that expression (9) requires, first, that both s and r be nonzero and, second, that both have the same sign. The latter can be supplanted by a stronger condition, however, that both must have a *positive* sign, that is, be positive motivations. To explain why, a text on difference equations[4] will show that in the equation earlier solved for m_1 and m_2, which we repeat for handy reference,

$$m^2 + (r + s - 1 - a) + a = 0 \tag{6}$$

a necessary condition for both roots (solutions for m) to be less than 1, and thus for the consumption path not to diverge, is that

$$1 + (s + r - 1 - a) + a > 0$$
$$s + r > 0 \tag{10}$$

4. S. Goldberg, *Introduction to Difference Equations* (New York: Wiley, 1958), p. 172.

What happens when this condition is not met is discussed under divergent behavior later. For present purposes, it rules out the possibility of finding any stable solution when both parameters are minus. But the condition in (9) would be violated if only one were minus. Therefore, one can say flatly that a normal path requires that both

$$r > 0 \quad \text{and} \quad s > 0 \tag{11}$$

What this condition comes down to is support for the libertarian instinct that normal behavior with respect to the vices of life requires not only "healthy resistance," for example, will power, but *also* "healthy temptation," for example, enjoying the vice as well. Lack of the latter positive motivation leads not just to the obvious result, aversion, but as we shall see in the case of alcoholics, to unobvious and bizarre divergence. So the inversions that the psychiatrist finds pathological, for example, drinking when one really wants *not* to, are mathematically pathological as well. (See, for example, shaded areas in Figure 5.)

Turning now to another requirement for normal behavior, texts like that cited above show another requirement for the quadratic equation (7) not to exceed $m = 1$, or reach an equivalent condition discussed below that equally throws the consumption path into divergent behavior. It translates in our model into the condition that

$$1 - a > 0$$
$$1 > a \tag{12}$$

or that the "accelerator," a, whereby increases in consumption cause further increase in consumption, not exceed 1. It can be shown that, when $a = 1$, consumption at time t is increased by ΔC_{t-1} because of this alone without our even considering extrinsic s and r motivations. When would that happen? One important class of cases is when the consumption of the previous period is *not eliminated* immediately, but remains in the body in the new period. An example is that alcohol is eliminated so slowly that measurements of blood alcohol (that is, as C) reflect not just the

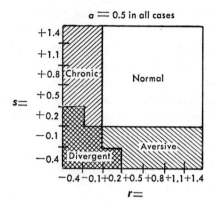

Figure 5

Consumption paths when $a = .5$ (computed for the selected values of r and s shown).

    Normal = reaches equilibrium between $C = 0$ and 1
   Aversive = reaches equilibrium with C below 0
   Chronic = reaches equilibrium with C above 1
 Divergent = monotonic divergence above any bounds
 Explosive = divergent oscillation (interpretation stops after initial collapse back toward negative)

current but the cumulative intake. This effect alone makes a near 1, and if we add to it any release from human caution, the result is a mathematical New Year's Eve discussed below as "explosive" behavior.

A final requirement in such a difference equation for normal consumption—that is, for the quadratic solutions for m_1 and m_2 in expression (7) not to exceed 1 and thus not lead to a divergent path of consumption—is shown in texts to be as follows:

$$1 - (s + r - 1 - a) + a > 0$$

$$1 + a > \frac{s + r}{2} \tag{13}$$

It means that the average extrinsic motivation parameter, $(s + r)/2$, must not be greater than $1 + a$. But since a must be less than 1, the average of the other two parameters must be less than 2. This is an idea like the danger of too much extrinsic "pressure" either for *or* against that activity. The consequences are not, however, what behavioral theories about these pressures purport to explain, for example, pathological kinds of chronic addictions. They are instead discussed below as "explosive" behavior, like overenthusiasm followed by quitting in disgust, for example, golf.

On the subject of "pressures," incidentally, we may rewrite (13) combined with the previous conditions that $1 > a$ and $s_a + r > 0$, so as to read

$$2 > 1 + a > \frac{s + r}{2} > 0 \tag{14}$$

$$1 > a > \frac{s + r}{2} - 1 > -1 \tag{15}$$

Now (15) implies that a, the acceleration effect, cannot be less than -1. A negative value of a has an interpretation like "conforming behavior." Namely, if consumption drops, one increases it; if it increases, one drops down again, as in conforming to a diet or social norms. What expression (15) says is that overconformity can, like overcorrecting a swerving car, itself destroy stability.

This example is a fitting symbol of all the requirements for normal consumption, summarized in (14) above. It takes moderation of *all* kinds—not just of the positive motivation like $+s$ and $+a$, but moderation in the restraining forces like $+r$ and $-a$ and avoidance of inversions (like $-s$)—in order to stay within a narrow path between 0 and 1 where the vices of life are the pleasures of living.

Chronic and Aversive Paths

Turning now to pathologies, consider the endless arguments of this form: Is alcoholism "really" addiction? Is chronic excess "really" alcoholism? Is the latter "any different" from ordinary drunkenness?[5] We now show how they differ.

For example, consider a distinction between two broad classes of pathologies. In one class there is no equilibrium and the path diverges to some kind of disaster; but since disaster cannot be tolerated chronically, consumption is episodic. In the other class, there *is* an equilibrium even if outside 1 or 0, and thus there is never a runaway disaster at any one moment; but precisely because there is equilibrium and no disaster to stop it, consumption is chronic.

The latter is obviously the character of chain-smoking, intractable obesity, the steady wine drinking of French alcoholics, and as the important case, narcotic addiction in its matured state, that is, now a chronic dependency. The necessary and sufficient condition to reach this kind of chronic equilibrium above the safe limit of 1 is

$$2 > 1 + a > \frac{s + r}{2} > 0 > r \qquad (16)$$

where the terms left of the zero simply repeat (14), the conditions in expressions (10), (12), and (13) for *any* equilibrium to be reached. On the right is the key new condition: $0 > r$. This is the condition, the others having given that some equilibrium is reached, for it to lie beyond the safe point. For, if the steady state is to be greater than 1, the *chronic* pathology, then

$$\frac{s}{s + r} > 1 \qquad (17)$$

which requires that r be minus and thus the denominator smaller than the numerator. (For if s were minus and larger than r, or both minus, it would violate the conditions for any equilibrium to be reached in (10) and lead not to the chronic but the divergent pathology discussed below.) Therefore, the essential condition for

5. A summary of these problems and an empirical classification close to the present logical one is in Jellinek, *op. cit.*

chronic pathology, of which drug addiction is the most prominent case, is simple: $0 > r$, or r negative. (See Figure 6.)

What does $-r$, "negative resistance," mean? Recall first of all that $+r$, or resistance, is what stops consumption in *proportion* to consumption; for example, it is satisfaction, then satiation, then sickness, and finally unconsciousness. Thus, the opposite of these, $-r$, is first of all a *tolerance* idea. It catches up the empirical truth that, for example, alcoholics become notoriously difficult to anesthetize and narcotic addicts become able to take several times the dose that is literally lethal to normal people.[6]

Second, since r applies in proportion to consumption—that is, the more consumption, the more satiation—then $-r$ reverses the sense of this statement—the more consumption, the more "negative satiation." What does this mean? A version of it in addiction is often loosely called "dependency," and thus $-r$ seems to be the logical equivalent of the famous tolerance-dependency syndrome. Here, however, it is necessary to become more precise than the literature on these topics often is about two logically very different things that may be meant by "dependency."

To use an example where the causes are visible, consider the "addiction to earning money" of a carpenter who takes extra jobs to earn $6,000 a year and of a stockbroker who takes extra fliers in the market to earn $600,000 a year. Suppose the carpenter's motivation is that he finds it an intolerable deprivation to drop below $6,000, as it would cost him, say, his family's home. Call this *withdrawal* dependency; that is, it is the pain of deprivation or fear of it. It is, logically, in the same category as narcotics.

The stockbroker is afflicted, however, with something else. Suppose that the more money he makes on the market, the easier it is to make still more; for example, he has more capital. It is like a hobby that has a negative cost. At the same time, the more capital he amasses, the more he *must* invest wisely to preserve it; but that simply makes still more capital, and so the process

6. For example, see *ibid.*

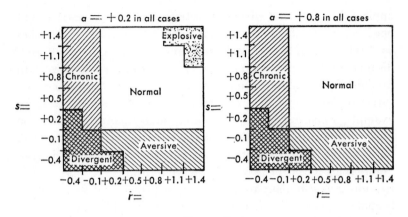

Figure 6

Consumption paths when $a = .2$ and when $a = .8$ (computed for the selected values of s and r shown).

feeds on itself. While the carpenter will stop when his withdrawal symptoms stop, for example, when he hits $8,000 a year and the family is no longer threatened, there is logically no stopping the stockbroker, for example, from going up into the millions. No good English word exists for the latter kind of dependency, the "negative cost" or "negative resistance" idea, but call it *insatiate* dependency.

Logically, the distinction is that the latter insatiate dependency is $-r$, which means a particular way it applies its motivational force. Recall that the part of the consumption equation where r applies is a subtraction from consumption (due to resistance) in proportion to consumption, that is, $-rC$. Normally, this is the "brake" on the process, but when this part of the logic is $-(-r)C = +rC$, it is a motivation increasing in proportion that one *is* consuming. This is a "runaway" idea. Taken alone, it implies no limit to how high C goes, for example, the stockbroker.

In contrast, the former kind of *withdrawal* dependency is logically $+s$, which means a different way in which motivation is applied. For note that withdrawal stress applies in proportion that one is *not* consuming. Therefore, it would be $+s$, since that applies as $+s(1 - C)$ in the original consumption equation. Now $1 - C$ disappears as consumption rises. That means $+s$ applies with diminishing force, for example, as the withdrawal symptoms are satisfied. Moreover, $(1 - C)$ turns *negative* if C goes over 1, for example, when one is now consuming more than his motivation for consuming required. Then, the sense of $+s$ becomes reversed, for example as if the withdrawal motivation originally is now "more than" or "over" satisfied. So the term $s(1 - C)$, previously the positive stimulant to increase, now turns negative and itself becomes a "brake." The previous runaway condition, due to $-r$, or lack of resistance, is checked. Therefore, $+s$, or withdrawal dependency, is not a runaway process even with pathological r or tolerance-dependency, but an implicit brake on consumption *beyond* the needed requirement, for example beyond the carpenter's needs or the addict's problem of calming withdrawal distress.

To express all this formally, recall that the conditions to reach the pathological equilibrium called "chronic" in (16) included

$$\frac{s + r}{2} > 0 > r \tag{18a}$$

$$s + r > 0 > 2r$$
$$s > -r > r \tag{18b}$$

where at the right in (18b) is another way of saying that in the chronic case r must be negative and the new point is that on the left. It is that for the chronic equilibrium to appear, s must be, first, positive in sign from (18a). Second, from (18b), s must be larger in absolute magnitude than r, that is, greater than either $-r$ or $+r$.

In a word, positive dependency of the *withdrawal* type, that is, $+s$, is what puts the "chronic" (equilibrium) into chronic addiction. Otherwise, chronic is identical to the divergent addictions like alcoholism in requiring the $-r$, or tolerance-insatiability, type of dependency.

Divergent Paths

All this is more paradoxical than it might seem. For $+s$ was a force increasing consumption—"stimulation"—in the original design of the model and its restraining role above in holding abnormal consumption to some equilibrium was completely unexpected. That result now suggests that the *absence* of $+s$, absence of positive "reasons" to consume, is going to have pathological consequences. An obvious case, of course, is the "aversive" path that reaches equilibrium below 0 because, with $-s$ substituted for s, then

$$0 > \frac{-s}{-s + r} \qquad (19)$$

when r is $+$ and greater in absolute magnitude than s. But the latter is no restriction because when it is not true, then a worse pathology develops that is as bizarre in real life as it is unexpected in the model.

It is well known[7] how prealcoholics gradually lose the capacity to stop at only chronic excess (equilibrium), and instead their episodes increasingly cross a line, as if the path crossed a ridge line, beyond which they do not return. (They go on to unconsciousness and hospitalization.) We say "cross a ridgeline," because there is precisely such a ridgeline in the model, namely, when m_1 or $m_2 = +1$.

Recall that, in the solution, below this point the consumption sequence m^k is decreasing, for example, if $m = .95$, the sequence is .95, .90, .86, ... But above $m = 1$, then m^k is an ever increasing consumption; for example, if $m = 1.05$, the sequence is 1.05, 1.10, 1.16, ... This means consumption going out of control, even if slowly, beyond any limit. Let us locate where this "ridgeline" is, short of which one returns, beyond never.

7. See, for example, A. D. Ullman, *To Know the Difference* (New York: St. Martin's Press, 1960).

Set the quadratic solution for m_1 and m_2 equal to exactly the critical value, $m = +1$, as follows:

$$+1 = \frac{-(r + s - 1 - a) \pm \sqrt{(r + s - 1 - a)^2 - 4a}}{2}$$

$$[2 + (r + s - 1 - a)]^2 = (r + s - 1 - a)^2 - 4a$$

$$4 + 4(r + s - 1 - a) = -4a$$

$$r + s = 0 \tag{20}$$

Thus, we now identify what an impending violation of the earlier condition for stability, $r + s > 0$ is tottering on the brink of: it is the "ridge," $m \geq +1$, beyond which the model goes into monotonic divergence, for example, the alcoholic, "loss-of-control" phenomenon that ends in a hospital. But what is surprising is *which* change in the motivations r and s pushes one over the brink. The rate of change in m with a change in r or s is a very complicated expression, but there is a simple way of circumventing it. Any text shows that in a quadratic equation of the form of (7) for the m's, two conditions are true of its roots, which translate into our parameters as

$$m_1(m_2) = +a \tag{21}$$

$$m_1 + m_2 = -(r + s - 1 - a) \tag{22}$$

Equation (21) indicates that both m's will have the same sign. If one m is positive and tending therefore toward monotonic divergence, the other will have the same tendency. Thus, we need not distinguish between them and can take the derivative (rate of change) of the second expression with respect to a positive change in the motivations, $s + r$:

$$\frac{d(m_1 + m_2)}{d(r + s)} = -1 \tag{23}$$

Therefore, the change that increases m_1 and m_2 and thus pushes them over the ridge into divergent consumption episodes would have to be a *decrease* in s and r until the disaster occurs when, effectively, both are zero or below!

The logical meaning of −*r* has already been discussed as "negative satiation." For example, of the two ideas American alcoholics mean by their old saying that, "One drink is too many; but if you take it, a thousand are not enough," the second phrase is the −*r* idea. But the first idea, "One drink is too many," expresses their aversion, or abstinence motivation, when sober. Now these rational reasons for remaining abstinent are logically −*s*. For example, desire for abstinence is a motivation applying fully when sober, that is, when 1 − *C* = 1, as −*s* would fully apply then. Yet we find, as the logical equivalent of the paradoxes in an alcoholic's behavior itself, that this −*s* state of *not* wanting to start consuming is implicated, when one does start, in producing the very disaster the −*s* state was motivation to avoid!

For the effect of plus changes in *s* on the size of the *m*'s is also

$$\frac{d(m_1 + m_2)}{d(s)} = -1$$

Therefore, the normal person's positive motivation, +*s*, *reduces* the *m*'s to stability; and the chronic person's positive *s*, even with

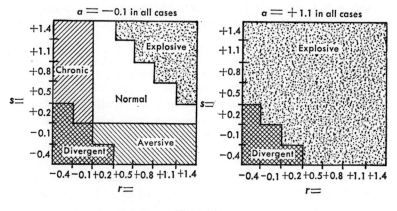

Figure 7

Consumption paths when *a* = −0.1 and when *a* = +1.1 (computed for the selected values of *s* and *r* shown).

pathological $-r$ dependency, also reduces the m's to stability even if at a socially unacceptable level. But combining the pathological $-r$ with *decreasing s*—for instance, rationality in wanting to avoid trouble would be $-s$ now—has opposite effects on the source of instability: it *increases* the m's. And when finally

$$0 > s + r \qquad (24)$$
$$-r > s$$

then $m > 1$, and former chronic case now begins to diverge into disastrous binges. Yet, how could *low* or "minus motivation" do this?

Empirically, it is just as puzzling. The binge or spree type of alcoholic usually has none of the obvious withdrawal stresses, at the time of the initial loss of control (although withdrawal stress will play a major role the next day). And as to the "reasons" for the initial loss of control, he often says he is as bewildered as everyone else, because he had no such intention. Indeed, who would *want* that kind of disaster? For example, to quote case reports common in the literature:

It was a hot day and I went in with him for no reason—not planned—and had a couple. The next thing I knew I woke up in a hotel room . . . .[8]

I don't drink every day and I'll go weeks without drinking. Then when I'm on top of the world and everything is going swell, I flop like a dope. What causes it I don't know! When I really *should* get drunk is after I've sobered up and I've got all kinds of problems. When I start drinking is, when I don't have any. Everything looks fine and rosy and everything.[9]

The sociologist citing the latter case says, for the nth time in his book, that alcoholics have ingenious "rationalizations" to obscure their real reasons for drinking. And psychiatrists say, by definition the person would not know his "unconscious" reasons. But if this logic is right, the alcoholics have been correct and our

8. *Ibid.*, p. 94.
9. *Ibid.*, p. 81.

behavioral second-guessing wrong. For, when the patients say they had *no* real reasons, at face value it means $s = 0$. And indeed, if they claim every reason *not* to desire such a disaster, it means s is negative. Then, given pathological $-r$ (presumably caused by past physiological abuse), this $-s$ condition of *not* wanting the runaway is precisely the condition for getting it!

If our logic is correct, then the reason all this is such an inexplicable paradox, at least to the alcoholics themselves even if no one else will believe them, is that in an important sense it *requires* no explanation. That is, it is expectable for "purely formal" reasons. Let us recall the simplified version of the consumption equation (2a), without details of time subscripts nor of specifying $i =$ intrinsic effect of consumption on itself. It was

$$\Delta C = (s + i)(1 - C) - (r - i)C \qquad \text{(normal)} \qquad (2c)$$

This we will call the "normal equation" when all parameters are positive. Now substitute $-r$ in place of r and call this the "chronic equation," or the model's version of the drug addict:

$$\begin{aligned} \Delta C &= (s + i)(1 - C) - (-r - i)C \\ &= (r + i)C - (s + i)(C - 1) \qquad \text{(chronic)} \qquad (2d) \end{aligned}$$

where rearranging in the lower form shows the "brake" we spoke of earlier, on the lower right. Namely, when consumption goes beyond 1, then the last term on the far right turns positive and now $+s$ and even the intrinsic effect, i, *resist* more consumption in proportion that consumption exceeds 1, just as for normal people $+r$ begins to resist in proportion that consumption substantially exceeds 0.

Now, continuing the pathological $-r$, next remove positive motivation to consume and replace it with desire to stay abstinent, by replacing s with $-s$ in the normal equation (2c). This yeilds the "divergent" equation, the model's version of the American alcoholic,

$$\begin{aligned} \Delta C &= (-s + i)(1 - C) - (-r - i)C \\ &= (r + i)C - (s - i)(1 - C) \qquad \text{(divergent)} \qquad (2e) \end{aligned}$$

Note that the lower right terms are the only possible "brake" on consumption. First, they imply the alcoholic need *not* lose control, as he sometimes does not. The conditions that he does not are, first, that i or intrinsic effects of alcohol in increasing its own consumption not be too large (or it would overwhelm s and turn the sense of the far right terms positive). Second, $1 - C$ must remain large; for example, he must limit himself to a few weak drinks, for, if and when consumption approaches 1, then $1 - C$ goes to zero, the right terms disappear, and "the brakes are gone." Finally, as C increases *above* 1, $1 - C$ turns negative and these brakes, the far right terms, become

$$-(s - i)(1 - C) = +(s - i)(C - 1)$$

where we mean that $C - 1$ is now positive. Now, with the whole conbination of terms preceded by a positive sign, unless the intrinsic effect i in accelerating consumption is extraordinarily high (enough to make the person sick, as discussed in the next section), all restraints are gone and the *entire* consumption equation has turned positive.

We can expect from such a diverging consumption path, incidentally, Jekyll-and-Hyde behavior. It makes a slow start with much protesting that little or no consumption is intended—for indeed, s *is* minus and the path has to be set into motion by some other circumstances (or by vacillation in s). But later, as consumption approaches $C = 1$, it will accelerate more rapidly than at the start and, after it passes that point $(C > 1)$, exhibit a wild "loss of control" as if giving the lie to the original protestations.

What is the behavioral interpretation of these Jekyll-and-Hyde evidences that the patient does not know his own "reasons"? To repeat, the formal logic suggests, precisely, that there need not *be* any reasons of the kind that require behavioral interpretation. The lack of physical restraints, the $-r$ condition, is distinctly abnormal. (No normal path can be produced without positive r.) *That* has to be explained. (The writer believes in the physiology of past abuse.) But the $-s$ condition is simply the absence of any positive motivation whose satisfaction would stop the process. It is logically like rockets going off into space: the phenomenon is spectacular, but once underway, it needs no positive motivation, only the lack of resistance. If other models confirm that this is a quite general consequence, then it means not to keep on looking endlessly for behavioral "reasons" for the alcoholic's loss-of-control phenomenon. Rather, we might have to face the awful truth that what the alcoholic has been saying for years is the truth: no "reason" is really necessary.

Explosive Paths

The problem instead is that, given the process in motion, it does not *stop* normally (the $-r$ mystery). Yet isn't this runaway condition also the effect of a, whereby consumption alone without other motivation accelerates itself? A crude paraphrase of much psychological thinking about addictions like obesity, alcoholism, and incipient narcotic use is that the person has emotional problems, these cause tensions, and it is the "release" from these ten-

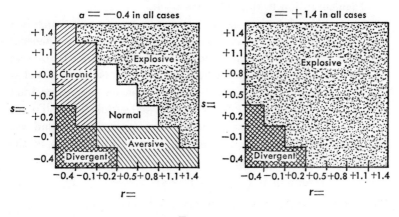

Figure 8

Consumption paths when $a = -0.4$ and when $a = +1.4$ (computed for the selected values of s and r shown).

sions, which the intake provides, that motivates still more intake. A caricature of this idea is the Hollywood hero who, when his girl leaves him, sets out to drown his sorrows and receives such a release from them that he goes on to become hilariously drunk . . . and then very sick and worse than sober.

The model reacts to the releasing effect, *a*, in the same way: It goes on a happy, Hollywood drunk that ends in sickness worse than sober. But, as serious students of the problem have asserted, psychiatrists have long failed to observe first hand[10] that this happy drunkenness no more resembles the unhappy American alcoholic off semiconscious in a hotel room for days or the French chronic case never sober for years than drinking on Tuesday morning resembles New Year's Eve. Drunkenness on the latter happy occasions and the Hollywood examples are instead "explosive" consumption paths. This term is Jellinek's expert classification of brief episodes that are socially destructive but medically nonpathological because, as abrupt explosions do, they end themselves. We now show that for practical purposes this outcome—the explosive episode that ends itself—is the effect of $+a$, that is, of consumption that accelerates itself.

First, when $1 > a > 0$, then *a* is only a source of controlled *oscillation*. For example, in drinking, this reproduces the normal behavior of getting "high" and then damping down to a safe equilibrium. But recalling expression (12), the condition $a > 1$ is a sufficient cause to throw the consumption off into some kind of unhappy ending other than the normal equilibrium. To see what that ending is, first recall in the solution for m_1 and m_2, the term under the radical, the radicand we will call q, in the quadratic formula. It was

$$q = (r + s - 1 - a)^2 - 4a \tag{25}$$

This is affected by a change in *a* in the following manner:

$$\frac{dq}{da} = 2(a - 1 - r - s) \tag{26}$$

10. Jellinek, *op. cit.*

Since the three terms on the right are negative, the effect of increases in a, symbolized by the left side, will be to make this radicand go down toward *negative* values. This would be so up to very large values of a (greater than $r + s + 1$), whereas we want to know what will happen as we pass the realistic point where pathology begins, $a = +1$. At that point, the quadratic radicand will be

$$q = (r + s - 2)^2 - 4 \qquad (a = 1)$$

which simplifies to

$$q = (r + s)(r + s) - 4(r + s) \qquad (27)$$

Therefore, the radical, q, can only remain positive in the unrealistic region beyond $r + s > 4$. Otherwise, it goes negative and this leads to complex roots involving $\sqrt{-1}$. We now show that in either event, it will be the same practical outcome. First, if the rare case $r + s > 4$ arises, then we recall from (22) that

$$m_1 + m_2 = -(r + s - 1 - a) \qquad (22)$$

and if we substitute in this, $s + r > 4$ and the critical value $a = +1$, the sum of the two m's will be below -2 and thus the largest m below -1. This leads, in such difference equations, to *divergent oscillation*.

This is a path of consumption that accelerates with extraordinary rapidity, as might be expected with $a = 1$ and s large. It accelerates so rapidly, indeed, that the path badly "overshoots" not only the region of its steady state but the safe limit $C = 1$ as well. But then it turns sharply and collapses back down into the negative regions below 0. We mercifully stop interpretation with the collapse, although technically the path would now cut a still wider swath through the regions of "negative consumption" (more sober than sober) and then burst out again. But the model's dynamics have no interpretation during trips through the negative region and instead we assume, as for normal cases, that the person can stop when the path returns through the normal region near zero. And the person would certainly *want* to stop then. For this sudden collapse, because the path rose too quickly, has no other interpretation than sickness.

We say collapse "because it rose too quickly" for the following reason. When we have normal $1 > a$, the path does not rise so quickly and, not accelerating itself so forcefully, does not over-shoot the steady state so far, the state toward which the normal parameters s and r are tending. The turnback, then, is not a col-lapse to the minus regions but damped oscillation under increas-ing control of the other parameters tending toward the steady state. The critical role of $a > 1$ in overpowering that normal tendency can be made formally clear by considering the second of the two possibilities before, by far the most usual one, when $4 > s + r$. In that case, which is the only realistic one of two possibilities outlined before, when the parameter $+a$ hits 1, the radicand turns negative and the solution now has to deal with $\sqrt{-1}$. In that event, texts[11] show that the solution for the con-sumption path, C_k, must be stated alternately as a sequence of the nonintuitive form

$$C_k = c_1 M^k \cos{(k\theta + c_2)} \qquad (28)$$

about which the only thing we need to know for present purposes is that the cosine function in the parentheses always oscillates between -1 and $+1$ and that this oscillation is *multiplied* by a "modulus" M^k. Thus, if M^k is a sequence going to zero with large k, it will be damped oscillation; but if M^k increases over time, it will be divergent oscillation. Hence, the issue is the same one as with m_1 and m_2 previously, whether the starting M is greater or lesser than 1. But it can be proved[12] that in our difference equation

$$M^2 = a$$
$$M = \pm\sqrt{a} \qquad (29)$$

And so it is very simple. The condition, $a > 1$, will lead to diver-gent oscillation—the explosive path that rises too quickly for its own good and then collapses to worse than sober. Thus, "releases"

11. Goldberg, *op. cit.*, pp. 138–142.
12. *Ibid.*, p. 172.

of the kind whereby consumption accelerates itself lead not toward marathon alcoholism, but in this logic only to Saturday-night explosions.

5. THE INSTABILITY OF SELF-REWARD

Before going on to consider a formal exception to the spirit of the last section, we digress to a related problem in social addictions like chess, music, and golf and in intellectual ones like learning mathematics or new research interests. Recall that in these activities, $+a$ had an interpretation, like ability to make rapid progress, whose effect is to *reward oneself* and thus motivate still more activity. Let these "self-rewarding" effects be E, as earlier, for example, a learner's visibly improving performance at some task, say golf. This improvement motivates more play, that increased practice leads to still more improvement, and so on. Figure 9 shows a curve of such self-rewarding improvements in performance during the "fever" of first mastering the skill.

The problem that Figure 9 makes obvious is that, if a learner is heavily dependent for motivation on rewarding himself by his own progress, that is, on $+a$, then one day this kind of motivation is inevitably going to "run out." For progress cannot continue over all bounds. Golf has built-in limits, learning becomes too time-consuming in relation to the relative increment of effect, and so on. As the path slackens its rate of climb, however, the intrinsic motivation due to progress drops off toward 0. For "progress motivation" depends on a rate of change. And if the only thing sustaining such an unusual level of activity, the "fever," was visible progress in mastering a new skill, now with that source of motivation running out, the path does not simply level out, but turns *down*.

The reason is that, on the way up, the enthusiast's high a carries him too far above the level of activity appropriate to s, his extrinsic reasons to devote only so much energy to this, and to r, the resistance of, say, too much cost in time or money. Again,

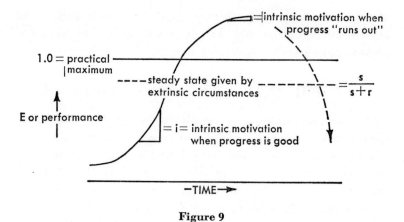

Figure 9

Learning that is dependent on progress for motivation.

with high a the model "overshoots" the steady state, $s/(s + r)$, that extrinsic circumstances alone would have permitted. If this overshooting is too great—which it is when $a > 1$—then when the reverse comes, the model does not damp down only to the steady state. Rather, at the very high level where progress is no longer possible, r resistances are now intolerable (because r applies in proportion to C, which activity is above normal maximum now). Therefore, with slackening of any motivational source, the level of activity is now sharply corrected by r. The person "comes to his senses"; for example, he now realizes all the time he has been spending on this activity and all the other things neglected. But as activity reduces, in most skills the rate of change in performance, for example, in golf scores, turns negative. What was previously interpreted as progress motivation, a, "the pride of accomplishment," now multiplies by *negative* change in accomplishment. Then this model, at least, goes into its disastrous collapse, after which we stop interpretation. In real life the outcome thereafter is varied, but the model behaves like the golfer who, once attaining the 70's at the height of his "fever" but whose scores are now ballooning to an inept 90, throws his clubs in the lake and, suddenly realizing all the r sacrifices this passion had been causing, quits. Similarly, the intellectual once a whiz in mathematics, or at playing the cello, now finds he is so much worse in both by his former standards that, rather than do them badly, he does them not at all.

In this sense, the kinds of native ability, enthusiasm, and "inner-directed" capacity to reward oneself by his own progress— all a qualities we admire—nevertheless share the episodic flavor of drunkenness and, over many such episodes, would tend toward dilettantism. Whereas, the "outer-directed" man, who contented himself in the first place with activity at only the rate appropriate to circumstances, $s/(s + r)$, is likely to be still at it today.

6. INTERACTION BETWEEN PARAMETERS

Finally, there is an interesting interaction between the effect of a and of $s + r$, to interpret which it is useful to return to the conventional addictions to narcotics and alcohol. Both start as "effect" phenomena. That is, before they become addictions, it is the physical or psychological effect of the intake that presumably motivates more intake (which accumulates in the body and therefore falls in the category of a, acceleration). Now, is it really impossible—as we implied in discussing Hollywood drunkenness and Saturday-night explosions—for this effect of a, alone, to produce the more pathological consumption paths, that is, that go beyond 1 and *stay* there?

The parameter a (and with it E, effect) has nothing to do with the "chronic" type of pathology in this model. For its steady state, $s/(s + r) > 1$, contains no a or E and is thus independent of them. But we can invent examples, even if at unrealistic magnitudes, where r and s are normal and an abnormal a, alone, can produce the monotonically divergent path. For example, if $r + s = 1$, then the condition $a > 4$ is just sufficient to prevent the quadratic radicand from going negative. Then the path goes up, straight up like a rocket, never to return. The conditions for this to happen within more realistic magnitudes are cumbersome to make meaningful, but their import is conveyed by rewriting (22) earlier to read

$$m_1 + m_2 = (a + 1) - (r + s) \tag{22a}$$

Recall that the sum, $m_1 + m_2$ would have to be positive and large, for example, near 2, to ensure that the largest m is over 1 and thus the path divergent without return. Suppose we start with a healthy person who has lots of "pressures" and "reasons" to consume, that is, s near 1. But he has normal physical reactions of nausea or of being anesthetized or drugged to unconsciousness when consumption gets too high; that is, he has r near 1. Then by (22a) the condition of large a around 1 or just beyond cannot do otherwise, "pressures" and "reasons" or not, than throw the path into normal or oscillating solutions that bring it *back*. This would be true unless $+a$ were some completely unrealistic value near 3 (roughly, acceleration three times each previous acceleration, which would be fatal).

Next, however, suppose the effect of strong s pressures and strong $+a$ gratifications is to make the person consume so much, so frequently, that in due time he develops tolerance; for example, as the Soviets report, the last stage before alcoholism is loss of the retching-nausea reaction, or gaining capacity to drink over it.[13] Formally, this means r is dropping toward 0. But as these physical changes take place, assume the person is psychologically *rational*. So, the effect of the constant disasters would be to reduce his motivation to consume when he is not doing so, for example, when sober or successfully withdrawn from narcotics. Formally, this rationality is s going to 0. Then he approaches the situation that, as

$$(s + r) \to 0,$$

then by (22a)

$$(m_1 + m_2) \to a + 1$$

13. Book review in *Quarterly Journal of Studies on Alcohol*, September, 1960.

As this condition approaches, the condition $a > 1$ could begin throwing him into monotonically divergent sprees before $s + r$ completely reached 0 (the condition that then guarantees disaster regardless of a). This is probably how it happens in real life, because case histories like Ullman's show that prealcoholics for some years, and probably preaddicts of drugs for a briefer time, display a transition period when loss of control is problematic and mixed with ordinary Saturday-night behavior.

Thus, while purely "effect" motivation in accelerating (accumulating) intake is not sufficient to produce other than Hollywood caricatures of alcoholism or addiction in a normal person with healthy s and r, it undoubtedly motivates the original excess consumption that later causes the deterioration, say, of r. And when that deterioration nears bottom—and the person now realizes he cannot stop (r near 0), so he does not want to start (s near 0)—then the only healthy thing he has left, the $+a$ gratification when he does start, can push him over the cliff.

Technical Note

Before passing on, the nonmathematical reader is reminded of other uses of this model. "Live" data illustrating an application of the model to small groups research are discussed below in Section 2, "Estimating Parameters." But first we sketch the model's solution in the deductive sense used above, namely, solving for the path of consumption over time. The sketch is brief, since we closely follow Goldberg,[14] whose book is particularly written for social scientists and explains details and gives many examples at each point sketched below.

1. SOLUTION FOR CONSUMPTION PATHS

We repeat for handy reference the "intrinsic effect" equation,

$$i = \frac{\Delta Et}{1 - E_t} = a(\Delta C_t) \qquad (1)$$

and then substitute the right-hand term for i in the "consumption equation," (2), where i was the effect of changes in consumption:

$$\Delta C_t = [s + a(\Delta C_{t-1})](1 - C_t) - [r - a(\Delta C_{t-1})]C_t \quad (2)$$

Now substituting at all points $\Delta C_t = C_{t+1} - C_t$, then expanding, it becomes

$$C_{t+1} - C_t = [s + a(C_t - C_{t-1}) - sC_t - aC_t(C_t - C_{t-1})] \\ - [rC_t - aC_t(C_t - C_{t-1})] \quad (30)$$

Collecting terms referring to the same time subscript, it reduces finally to

$$C_{t+1} = (1 + a - s - r)C_t - aC_{t-1} + s \qquad (31)$$

Advancing time by $+1$ period and shifting terms, we can rewrite this as

$$C_{t+2} + (s + r - 1 - a)C_{t+1} + aC_t = s \qquad (32)$$

14. *Op. cit.*

This is the standard form of a linear, second-order difference equation with constant coefficients; reduced to this form, its solution can easily be followed by the reader. Without the detailed rationale given by Goldberg,[15] a brief sketch of the steps follows.

First, we will need one "particular" solution, namely, some constant C that, when substituted in (32) above, gives a steady state $C_{t+2} = C_{t+1} = C_t = C$. To find the latter, substitute the constant C for all C's in (32) and solve for C:

$$C + (s + r - 1 - a)C + aC = s$$

$$C = \frac{s}{s + r} \tag{33}$$

This steady state plays the role in the solution of a constant determining the general "level" of activity, to which variable terms are added, for example, as the constant b does in $y = ax + b$. To find the other variable terms, set the left side of (32) equal to zero:

$$C_{t+2} + (s + r - 1 - a)C_{t+1} + aC_t = 0 \tag{32a}$$

and call this (32a), the "homogenous" version of (32). While it is not intuitive, the varying terms we seek can be shown[16] to be solutions satisfying this homogenous equation. There are two such solutions. Two can be found by assuming that we start at C_0 with some arbitrary consumption, c. Then suppose C_t at each time is some fraction or multiple, m, of consumption at the previous time. Therefore, $C_0 = c$, $C_1 = mc$, $C_2 = m(mc) = m^2c$, and so on until $C_t = m^t c$. Substituting this expression for C_t in (32a), we get

$$cm^{t+2} + (s + r - 1 - a)cm^{t+1} + acm^t = 0$$

and dividing through by the common factor, cm^t, gives

$$m^2 + (s + r - 1 - a)m + a = 0 \tag{32b}$$

15. *Ibid.*, Chapters 3 and 4.
16. *Ibid.*, pp. 121–135.

which (32b) is called the "auxiliary" equation corresponding to (32). This equation is easily solved by the quadratic formula

$$m_1 \text{ or } m_2 = \frac{-(s + r - 1 - a) \pm \sqrt{(s + r - 1 - a)^2 - 4a}}{2} \quad (34)$$

Both roots yielded by the positive and the negative signs attached to the radical satisfy (32a) in the form $C_t = m_1{}^t \text{ or } m_2{}^t$. Texts show that the "general" solution to (32a) is simply to add these two solutions:

$$C_t = c_1 m_1{}^t + c_2 m_2{}^t$$

prefaced by arbitrary constants, c_1 and c_2, which mean only that any number of arbitrary starting points are covered by the formula. Then if we add, to these two solutions to the homogenous equation, the steady-state constant, $s/(s + r)$ satisfying the complete equation, we get

$$C_t = c_1 m_1{}^t + c_2 m_2{}^t + \frac{s}{s + r} \quad (35)$$

This can be shown to be the solution, not to the homogenous version, but now to the complete model (32) itself. Therefore, while its textbook rationale has not been expanded here in detail, the result is simple: the complete solution is, in effect, a sum of particular solutions.

2. ESTIMATING PARAMETERS

Since the only minor difficulty in use of the above—namely, when the quadratic formula results in $\sqrt{-1}$ and a trigonometric solution must be used—is covered in detail in Goldberg, we take up here a problem that is not: estimating parameters. If the consumption path is fully observed from the start and data are infallible—in theory, that is—this would not be difficult. For example, it can be shown that $C_1 = s$. But one would not trust this for real human consumption paths, which would never follow this model exactly from the start. Instead, we need methods of estimating parameters that reflect larger amounts of information about the matured path.

For this purpose, write equation (31) for any three periods, t to $t + 2$, as

$$C_{t+2} = (1 + a - s - r)C_{t+1} - aC_t + s \qquad (36)$$

$$C_{t+1} = (1 + a - s - r)C_t - aC_{t-1} + s \qquad (37)$$

$$C_t = (1 + a - s - r)C_{t-1} - aC_{t-2} + s \qquad (38)$$

These are three linear equations in three unknowns, and can be solved in the usual manner. Subtract (37) from (36) and subtract (38) from (37) to eliminate s. Then multiply each of the results of these subtractions by the coefficients of $(1 + a - s - r)$ in the other. Then the resulting products can be subtracted to eliminate $(1 + a - s - r)$. This leaves an equation entirely in a, which can be written, with $C_{t+1} - C_t = \Delta C_t$, as follows:

$$a = \frac{\Delta C_{t+1} \Delta C_{t-1} - (\Delta C_t)^2}{\Delta C_{t-2} \Delta C_t - (\Delta C_{t-1})^2} \qquad (39)$$

This is an interesting concept and index on its own right, for research otherwise not concerned with the present model. Suppose we have records of activity over time, anything from the amount a person speaks per minute in small group sessions, to the investments of a corporation per year in research and development, to historical records of some activity of a whole society per decade. These can be characterized by the coefficient a, by using expression (39) above or its more stable analogs below. In such applications, an outcome of $+a$ would indicate a motivation like, say, "enthusiasm"; that is, positive increases in activity generate still more activity. Whereas an outcome of $-a$ would indicate motivation like, say, "conformity"; that is, slacking off of previous activity is what generates more activity. The latter would pick out, for example, the student who studies hard only when he falls behind but slacks off when he has caught up. Or as another example, $+a$ suggests "fashions" in activity; that is, activity generates itself. Whereas $-a$ suggests that the activity is prompted by previous neglect of activity, for example, getting a haircut or shopping for clothing.

Given a, it is easy to find s. Multiply (36) and (37) each by the coefficient of $(1 + a - s - r)$ in the other and then subtract (37) from (36) to eliminate $(1 + a - s - r)$. The result comes down to

$$s = \frac{C_{t+2}C_t - (C_{t+1})^2 - a(C_{t+1}C_{t-1} - C_t{}^2)}{C_t - C_{t+1}} \tag{40}$$

This is a measure of, for example, desire to avoid complete deprivation from the activity or consumption, s applying in proportion to $1 - C$. For example, in panel records of consumer purchases, $+s$ might perhaps be interpreted as real needs for the product, that is, as corrective action whenever one gets low on it.

In any event, with s and a now known, any of the three original equations gives r; for example, using (37) gives

$$r = 1 + a - s + \frac{s - C_{t+1} - aC_{t-1}}{C_t} \tag{41}$$

As Figure 3 illustrates, this expression is a good measure of the difficulty of an activity. For example, golf, tennis, and chess would show high $+r$, bowling, ping-pong, and checkers lower r.

While we motivate the substantive significance of the *concepts* above, unhappily it is another story for the statistical significance of the particular measures proposed. As the worst example, if a consumption (or activity) path is approaching anywhere near steady state, then expression (39) approaches

$$\frac{0 - 0}{0 - 0}$$

for reliable data and

$$\frac{\text{error} - \text{error}}{\text{error} - \text{error}}$$

for fallible data. An alternative suggested by John Gilbert is to note that our expression for, say, C_{t+3}, can be visualized as

$$C_{t+3} = b_{32.1}C_{t+2} + b_{31.2}C_{t+1} + b \tag{42}$$

or as an auto-regression problem (in which the independent variables are simply the lagged states of the dependent variable). We understand that there are unresolved statistical issues in this procedure that have been discussed in economics,[17] but the procedure itself is simple. We carry out the usual multiple regression analysis and then identify our parameters from expressions like (36) as

$$s = b$$
$$a = -b_{31.2}$$
$$r = 1 + a - s - b_{32.1}$$

An Example

We illustrate with data that can*not* be fitted by this model, and are for that reason instructive. They are from a small-groups experiment, and its connection to "addiction" is this: Take the expanded form of the consumption equation, expression (30), and collect terms for each parameter. It becomes, surprisingly,

$$\Delta C_t = s(1 - C_t) - rC_t + a(\Delta C_{t-1}) \tag{30a}$$

We say "surprisingly," because, as mentioned in footnote 3, for all the original motivation of this as an addiction model, expression (30a) turns out to be about as neutral or "contentless" a scheme as one could think of, say, for analyzing the statistics of *any* path that one has reason to believe is heavily governed by

17. Our attention was called by Clifford Hildreth to these references: H. B. Mann and A. Wald, "On the Statistical Treatment of Linear Stochastic Difference Equations," *Econometrica*, 11 (July–October, 1943), 173–200 (reprinted in *Selected Papers in Statistics and Probability* by Abraham Wald, New York: McGraw-Hill, 1955); Leonid Hurwicz, "Least Square Bias in Time Series," in *Statistical Inference in Dynamic Economic Models*, Monograph No. 10, Cowles Commission for Research in Economics, Tjalling C. Koopmans, ed. (New York: Wiley, 1950).

Mann and Wald show that the classic regression method is also the maximum-likelihood (efficient) estimate for the auto-regression problem. But Hurwicz shows that the result is biased in the common cases he examines, the bias in his cases being 10–25 per cent of the value of the parameters, in the direction of reducing their absolute magnitudes (reducing oscillation in our model).

its own previous states. For example, the first two terms on the right are familiar in learning models.

Hence, our hope that the scheme would be useful in analyzing small-group data, which typically take the form of paths, for example, discussion, that are governed by their own previous states, for example, previous remarks. In the example conveniently at hand, however, the observations are a week apart; and, as we shall see, that is stretching continuity a bit far. The data in Table 2 come from a study of *developmental* processes in three-man groups, from originally *ad hoc* groups to, sometimes, highly effective teams. The subjects are college students, and the experimental task they are given is investing in a stock market, indeed, an actual market created largely by their own transactions each

Table 2

Weekly Measures in Small-Group Experiment[a]

	Group Cohesiveness[b]		Task Policy (Investment)[c]		Task Success (Gain)[d]	
Week	Success-ful Group:	Unsuccess-ful Group	Success-ful Group	Unsuccess-ful Group	Success-ful Group	Unsuccess-ful Group
1	.644	.551	.493	.640	.301	.224
2	.667	.045	.512	.575	.250	.111
3	.622	.294	.578	.535	.178	.049
4	.585	.282	.247	.629	.234	.074
5	.654	.581	.246	.762	.248	.116
6	.555	.486	.555	.894	.234	.252
7	.114	.466	.755	.744	.158	.201
8	.596	.084	.788	.520	.221	.163
9	.557	.600	.970	.990	.454	.258
10	.735	.312	.920	.498	.446	.225

a. Data are thanks to Professor John Kennedy, Fredrick Kling, and Diana Lees of the Department of Psychology, Princeton, from its "So Big" experiments in developmental processes in groups. (The first ten weeks of 1961–62 experiments simply happened to be that processed by the time of this analysis.)

b. Cohesiveness = "friendliness," "cooperation," etc., measured by an index developed from factor analysis. Here 0 = lowest, 1 = highest possible.

c. Task policy = commitment to investment in stocks (as opposed to holding cash), e.g., an optimism or risk-taking policy. Here 0 = legal minimum, 1 = maximum.

d. Task success = accumulated net gain or profit by the period in question. Here 0 = minimum, 1 = maximum observed by end of experiment, rounded to next $100,000.

e. Successful group is Syracuse, which ended experiment (subsequently) first of ten teams. Unsuccessful group is Athens, which ended last of ten.

week over fourteen weeks. Illustrative data are for the team that *subsequently* proved most successful (of ten teams) in the market versus the team least successful, during the first ten weeks they were evolving their working methods. Indicators analyzed by this model were a composite measure of group cohesion (for example, cooperativeness), an indicator of task policy (preference for stocks rather than cash), and an objective measure of task success (accumulated net gain by each period). These measures are due, with gratitude, to the sources named in Table 2.

Table 3 gives parameter "estimates" by the formulas (39), (40), and (41) for successive five-week segments, then their averages, then the results from a regression analysis by (42) for the whole ten weeks. The last is most comparable to the average just above it in Table 3, excluding the two worst cases, where the denominators in expressions like (39) are smallest (which has the illusory effect of making parameters largest!). Discrepancies be-

Table 3

Parameter Estimates for "Cohesion"

	a		s		r	
Algebraic (5 weeks)	Success-ful Group	Un-success-ful Group	Success-ful Group	Un-success-ful Group	Success-ful Group	Un-success-ful Group
Weeks 1–5	1.6	−1.3	1.6	− .6	.9	−2.4
2–6	.2	−1.2	1.7	.3	1.1	− .2
3–7	a	.2	a	.7	a	.8
4–8	6.0	−2.4	3.9	−4.7	2.9	−4.4
5–9	.9	−4.4	1.2	−1.3	1.6	− .5
6–10	− .4	1.0	.3	1.2	.0	2.1
Averages of:						
Median two	1.22	−1.26	1.66	− .12	1.34	− .35
Lowest four in absolute magnitude[a]	.57	− .34	1.22	.41	.90	.55
Regression	.09	.00	.61	.45	.48	.73

a. Unusual absolute magnitudes are indicative of insignificant denominator in expression (39). For this reason, where solutions are missing, a would have been greater than ±10.

tween the latter two averages, the absurd instability of the detailed results, and finally the fact that neither can be made wholly to fit the actual paths in Table 2, illustrate the unsolved problems in estimation to characterize such "unruly" social data.

These data are for "cohesion," probably the *least* stable measure. And all indications are that the parameters (forces) affecting cohesion are changing—indeed, the whole purpose of the experiments is to study how *ad hoc* groupings of individuals *do* change in the developmental processes out of which an effective (or ineffective) team develops. In order to diagnose that kind of problem, surely the best procedure would be to do the regression analysis for shorter periods, as we did the algebraic solutions, since the averaging implicit in regression estimates for the whole ten weeks introduces a highly misleading picture of *small* parameters that, when used to calculate a theoretic path, (1) make it more monotonic and (2) cause it to damp out faster than actual paths. (Hurwicz[18] conjectures this as the consequence of biases in the regression procedure itself. This is true, but of small magnitude compared with the averaging effects above, which are, of course, correctable by using shorter periods.) The algebraic solutions for short periods have the opposite error—if they are taken seriously at all—of "blowing up" parameters too large. But for illustration, taking them as resembling what careful regression analysis of short periods would show, one might be interested in the following kinds of interpretations:

1. Signs of parameters almost never change for the successful group, but frequently do for the unsuccessful one, perhaps suggesting that the former is well organized, the latter *ad hoc*.

2. Parameters for the successful group are almost never negative, for the unsuccessful one usually so. The former leads to stable or "normal" paths, we know analytically, the latter to unstable pathologies.

18. *Op. cit.*

Table 4

Parameter Estimates for Task (Investment) Policy

Algebraic (5 weeks)	a Successful Group	a Unsuccessful Group	s Successful Group	s Unsuccessful Group	r Successful Group	r Unsuccessful Group
Weeks 1–5	.9	1.8	.8	1.3	1.3	− .1
2–6	.9	.4	.6	.2	.7	.9
3–7	.3	7.1	.5	.8	.2	1.3
4–8	−1.2	1.4	1.4	1.6	.1	.6
5–9	−1.0	2.3	.6	3.0	− .1	.9
6–10	.2	.9	1.3	2.4	.1	1.0
Averages of:						
Median two	.23	1.61	.73	1.45	.16	.86
Four lowest in absolute magnitude	.58	1.13	.63	.97	.10	.56
Regression (all weeks)	.40	− .09	.25	.88	.13	.37

Computer regression programs could easily carry out the calculations (and for *all* the ten groups involved) required to examine such interpretations seriously.

Table 4 gives comparable "solutions" characterizing the two groups' investment policy. Illustrative diagnoses, if serious analysis produced results like these, might be as follows:

1. The successful group's investment path is characterized by moderate, the unsuccessful one by immoderate, *sizes* of parameter. The former suggest stability, for example, "policy," the latter instability, for example, "wildness."

2. The successful investment path is characterized by diminishing r; the unsuccessful one is not. Here this means diminishing "fear of the market," that is, decreasing resistance to investment.

The last point has an interesting consequence if we could take these illustrations as serious results (as they are not). Point 2, the successful group's full-investment policy, has an unstabilizing

Table 5

Parameter Estimates for "Success" (Cumulative Gain)

Algebraic (5 weeks)	a Successful Group	a Unsuccessful Group	s Successful Group	s Unsuccessful Group	r Successful Group	r Unsuccessful Group
Weeks 1–5	.5	.5	.4	−.3	1.5	−2.2
2–6	.2	−.5	.1	−.1	−.1	−2.3
3–7	1.3	a	−.5	a	−1.4	a
4–8	5.3	.4	1.4	.3	4.7	1.6
5–9	3.2	.8	1.0	.7	3.5	2.6
6–10	2.5	1.2	.7	.6	2.1	1.4
Averages of:						
Median two	1.91	.64	.57	.49	1.82	1.49
Four lowest in absolute magnitude	1.14	.29	.18	.14	.54	−.38
Regression (all weeks)	1.64	.36	.48	.11	1.49	.53

a. Estimate of a over 10, denominator of expression (39) negligible.

effect on its net gain, which is now implied by the parameter estimates in Table 5.

The path that the estimates of Table 5 characterizes, cumulative net gain or profit (which we, and not necessarily the experimenters, use as an indicator of task success) is a proper kind of variable for this model. Our theory is meant to portray only *differences* from the previous state, not the magnitude of a whole new quantity generated rather independently of the last quantity (as "cohesion" measured in a new session after a week has intervened would tend to be a new quantity). In any event, the estimates for cumulative net gain in Table 5 are more in accord with each other and all suggest something surprising about the successful group's success.

Recall the classic story of the tortoise and the hare. It is always debatable whether brief success during a period of experimental observation, for example, in test marketing a new product, is going to be borne out in the long pull. Therefore, a convenience of any model like this is that its solutions (good estimates of them would) suggest the future steady state, here $s/(s + r)$. Surprisingly, both the algebraic and regression estimates of this ratio for the successful group show that group's prognosis to be *poor* (not significantly different in $s/(s + r)$ from the other group, which was in the last place of ten teams most of the time). Why, then, in the culminating weeks of the experiment, after our analysis was done, did the group here called "successful" shoot up spectacularly, thereby taking first place? The experimenters have kindly supplied the subsequent data given in Table 6.

We cannot duplicate the exact timing of the left figures of interest here, but their extreme magnitude is, curiously, just what would be predicted from the parameters of the previous ten weeks. For, the successful group's net gain had been, since the first few weeks, going into *divergent oscillation*.

This is apparent in the solutions for a. Combined with a small s and large r, such a process has trouble getting off the ground at first, and the amplitude of oscillation is therefore small at first. But when it finally reaches magnitudes like those at the end of ten weeks, the next surge will be a real boom—and the next after that a worse bust! Or vice versa, because the divergent oscillation we get formally was apparently, in the real experiment, an interaction between this group's unusual full-investment policy (including maximum use of credit to buy stocks) and oscillations the experimenters were introducing into the market. A "recovery"

Table 6

Success (Net Gain)

Week	Successful Group	Unsuccessful Group
11	.480	.233
12	.727	.258
13	.745	.219
14	.813	.235

in the final market was apparently multiplied in amplitude by this group's maximum stock commitment. But if the experiment had closed on a *down* oscillation, then, if we are to believe this model, our "most successful" group might have ended up as the flashy hare surpassed by even our slowest tortoise.[19]

19. The actual experimenters are well aware of these problems, of course, and have abundant other criteria of task effectiveness, itself not the main object of study. But in many test and evaluation situations where data are scanty and first-hand observation impossible, "detecting the Hare" is indeed a serious problem. Our other solutions, incidentally, suggest the successful group *was* effective, that is, cohesive, stable, and with definite policy. So, it may have guessed, correctly, the experiment would end on an upswing.

Name Index

Subject Index